OFF THE GROUND

AN ANTHOLOGY OF POETRY

Compiled by

WILLIAM KERR, M.A.

LATE

DIRECTOR OF STUDIES, THE TRAINING COLLEGE, GLASGOW

Author of " The English Apprentice "

and

ALEXANDER HADDOW, B.A.

LATE

PRINCIPAL MASTER OF METHOD, THE TRAINING COLLEGE, GLASGOW

*Author of " On the Teaching of Poetry " and " The Ring and the
Book as a Connected Narrative"*

BOOK II

Granger Index Reprint Series

BOOKS FOR LIBRARIES PRESS

FREEPORT, NEW YORK

STANDARD BOOK NUMBER:
8369-6067-X

LIBRARY OF CONGRESS CATALOG CARD NUMBER:
76-75516

PREFACE

" Poesy only instructs as it delights."—*John Dryden.*

" The end of writing is to instruct ; the end of poetry is to instruct
by pleasing."—*Samuel Johnson.*

Those sentences, we hope, are an indication at once of the purpose
and the plan of this anthology. In making it we have been guided
by one consideration—the aesthetic value of each poem for the
readers we have in view. Of our notes we would merely say what
will be immediately obvious, that we have made no attempt to
construct lessons. We believe, indeed, that for every poem taught
many should be read aloud, and that very often a beautiful and
sympathetic reading will teach more than all the commentators.
Naturally, therefore, we hold that no book can take the place of the
teacher, whose ultimate aim is to lead pupils to enjoy reading
poetry for themselves.

We wish to thank all who have so generously assisted us, especially
Miss M. L. Chisholm, Mr. J. F. A. Burt, and Mr. A. D. Campbell
for their reading of proofs and their valuable comments.

W. K.
A. H.

Our method of collaboration is that each undertakes a book,
relying upon the other for all the help and encouragement that
criticism and suggestion can give. The final responsibility for
this book is mine.

W. K.

ACKNOWLEDGMENTS

We value highly the permission to include copyright material in this anthology, and are happy to put on record our indebtedness for :

"THE DANCING STAR" to Mr. Douglas Ainslie, and "The Fortnightly Review".

"SCHULE IN JUNE" to Mr. Robert Bain.

"MATILDA" to Messrs. Gerald Duckworth & Co.

"AN OLD WOMAN OF THE ROADS" to Mr. Padraic Colum and Messrs. MacMillan & Co., Ltd.

"ROUNDABOUTS AND SWINGS" to Mr. Patrick Chalmers and Messrs. Methuen & Co., publishers of "Blue Days and Green Days".

"LEISURE" to Mr. W. H. Davies, and Messrs. Jonathan Cape, Ltd., publishers of the Poems of W. H. Davies.

"A FANCY FROM FONTENELLE" to Mr. Alban Dobson, representative of the author's trustees, and The Oxford University Press.

"LORD ARNALDOS" to the author's executrix and Messrs. Martin Secker and Warburg, Ltd., publishers of "The Collected Poems of James Elroy Flecker".

"THE FALLOW DEER AT THE LONELY HOUSE" to the author's executors and Messrs. MacMillan & Co., Ltd., publishers of "The Collected Poems of Thomas Hardy".

"TEWKESBURY ROAD" and "SEA FEVER", reprinted from "Collected Poems of John Masefield" (William Heinemann, Ltd.) by permission of the author.

"NICHOLAS NYE" to Mr. Walter de la Mare and Messrs. Constable & Co.

"LONE DOG" to Mrs. Irene de Selincourt.

"MILK FOR THE CAT" to Mrs. Harold Monro and The Poetry Bookshop.

"JOHN O' LORN" to the author's trustees and Messrs. Wm. Blackwood & Sons, Ltd., publishers of "The Poetry of Neil Munro".

"THE FIGHTING TÉMÉRAIRE" and "HAWKE" to Sir Henry Newbolt and Mr. John Murray, publisher of "Poems New and Old".

"THE FIFTEEN ACRES" to Mr. James Stephens and Messrs. MacMillan & Co., Ltd., publishers of "Collected Poems".

"THE BALLAD OF SEMMERWATER" to Lady Watson.

"THE LAKE ISLE OF INNISFREE" to Mr. W. B. Yeats and Messrs. MacMillan & Co., Ltd., publishers of "Collected Poems".

"LATE AUTUMN" to Mr. Andrew Young.

CONTENTS

CONTENTS—continued

INDEX OF AUTHORS

OFF THE GROUND

TO EACH AND EVERY READER

The poems have been chosen for this book with one aim only—your pleasure in reading them, and thinking about them, and reading them again. The questions and notes are intended to suggest ways of reading and thinking to you. Some of them may lead you to put other questions to yourself. It is hoped that when you have answered them all—these here and your own—you will enjoy still more the poems to which they refer.

But remember that, unlike questions in arithmetic, questions on poetry may frequently have more than one right answer. We are not allowed to form our own opinions on how many 9's make 63, but we may—indeed, we must—decide for ourselves whether Mr. Davies in " Leisure " is right in demanding time to stand and stare, and whether out of this demand he has made a good poem. It would be as absurd to say that we must like a certain poem as it would be to say that we must like certain colours, or foods, or faces.

None the less, however widely we may differ as to the merits of particular poems, most of us will admit that poetry in general has qualities that interest us and delight us.

Often we have the pleasure of a well-told story. Given a suitable theme, a poet can usually make more of it than a prose writer can. He has his rhymes and his swinging lines to help him, and he can say things in a bold and memorable way. Read the plain prose version of " Lochinvar " (page 87) and note how much you lose.

Most poems contain bright and fresh word-pictures. The poet has, like the painter, the gift of seeing the beauty of the world, and, in place of the painter's palette, he has his own vivid language to paint what he sees. His pictures, if we study them carefully, become our own possessions, seen by the mind's eye, and brought back again at will. They enrich us, even as the host of golden daffodils brought wealth to William Wordsworth (see page 94). Read "A Song" and "November Days" (page 45) and study the pictures they put before you. For richer colours, read "The Lady of Shalott" (page 108). For colours and forms that defy the painter, read "La Belle Dame sans Merci" (page 120).

The poet is musician as well as story-teller and painter, the best equipped of all writers to make a joyful noise. His sensitive ear enables him to choose the most melodious words and arrange them in the best-sounding order. Listen to the water-music of "A Song" (page 45) and "The Lake Isle of Innisfree" (page 131).

There are at the poet's command, moreover, two excellent musical devices, rhyme and regular rhythm. From infancy, almost, most people have liked word-jingles or rhymes. If Little Jack Horner had sat on a sofa, eating his Christmas pie, and had put in his thumb, and pulled out a raisin, and missed out the rhymes like this, we should have taken very little interest in him. Rhyme is not found in all poetry, but most poets have been glad of it, and have often used it, as you will discover, in subtle and telling ways. Meanwhile, read aloud "Sea-weed" (page 48). Observe how the rhymes take hold of you, and almost by themselves produce the storm-notes of the poem.

To understand rhythm, we must first observe that in all our speech we pronounce, or stress, some syllables more emphatically than others. In prose those emphatic syllables—let us call them "beats"—fall haphazardly, as in the lines above, but poets long ago learned that, by choosing and arranging their words so that the beats occurred at various regular intervals, they could produce definite metres, or rhythms, to which their poems marched, or danced, or cantered, or galloped, or, it might be, swung like the waves of the sea.

"The Neckan" marches.

> *Of earth, of earth the Neckan sings,*
> *He hath no other tale.*
>   page 127

" The Fifteen Acres " dances.

> *I flit and twit*
>
> *In the sun for a bit*
>
> *When his light so bright is shining, O.*   page 90

" The Priest and the Mulberry Tree " canters.

> *Did you hear of the curate who mounted his mare,*
>
> *And merrily trotted along to the Fair?*   page 32

" The Good News " gallops.

> *I sprang to the stirrup and Joris and he;*
>
> *I galloped, Dirck galloped, we galloped all three.*   page 133

" Hawke " swings like the waves.

> *But they took the foe for pilot and the cannon's glare for light*
>
> *When Hawke came swooping from the West.*   page 21

Those are examples, only, of the rhythms that poets have made, and that you will hear as you read this book. It is always interesting to ask why a poet has chosen a certain rhythm for a poem, and always a pleasure to find the answer to one's question.

This may be the last and most important of our discoveries. We shall find that we like a poem not only because of what it says, and not only because of how it says it. Our enjoyment of its " story " is mingled with our pleasure in the poet's vivid words, clear rhymes, appropriate rhythms. Our pleasure in words and rhymes and rhythms comes not from themselves, but from the use the poet has made of them in his poem. This truth will come back to us whenever, at the end of our study, and assisted by it, we read a poem aloud as intelligently and sympathetically as we can. For this final reading all our work may be regarded as preparation, and, in this reading, if we express something of the beauty of the poem, we are, for the time being, poets, too.

13

LEISURE

What is this life if, full of care,
We have no time to stand and stare?

No time to stand beneath the boughs
And stare as long as sheep or cows.

No time to see, when woods we pass,   5
Where squirrels hide their nuts in grass.

No time to see, in broad daylight,
Streams full of stars, like skies at night.

No time to turn at Beauty's glance,
And watch her feet, how they can dance.   10

No time to wait till her mouth can
Enrich that smile her eyes began.

A poor life this if, full of care,
We have no time to stand and stare.

WILLIAM H. DAVIES
(*20th Century*)

1. We are to stare as long as sheep or cows. What are we
   to gain by our staring?
2. Line 13. Why is life poor without leisure?
3. Write out lines 3-6. Then read them aloud and put this
   mark, /, above each syllable on which your voice lays
   stress. You will find there are four stresses or " beats "
   in each line.
4. Why did the poet write this poem in little stanzas of
   two lines (couplets)?
5. Suggest themes for couplets similar to the poet's third
   and fourth. Try to make for yourself a " No time "
   couplet in his rhythm.
6. Why has this poem been placed at the beginning of your
   book?

Notes: page 141.

THE COUNTRY LAD

Who can live in heart so glad
As the merry country lad,
Who upon a fair green baulk
May at pleasure sit and walk,
And amid the azure skies 5
See the morning sun arise—
While he hears in every spring
How the birds do chirp and sing—
Or before the hounds in cry
See the hare go stealing by ; 10
Or, along the shallow brook,
Angling with a baited hook,
See the fishes leap and play
In a blessed sunny day ;
Or to hear the partridge call 15
Till she have her covey all ;
Then the bee to gather honey ;
And the little black-haired coney
On a bank for sunny place
With her forefeet wash her face ? 20

Are not these with thousands moe
Than the courts of kings do know
The true pleasing spirit's sights
That may breed true loves delights ?

Nicholas Breton
(1542-1626)

baulk : *ridge of land left unploughed*
coney : *rabbit*　　moe : *more*

1. Show that this country lad *has* time to stand and stare.
2. Does Breton hold the same opinions as Davies (page 14) ?
3. What use does each poet make of word-pictures ?
4. Which of Breton's pictures might Davies have used in
   " Leisure " ?
5. (*a*) Mark the " beats " in lines 1-4. (See page 14, question 3.)
   (*b*) What difference do you find between the pace of this
   poem and that of " Leisure " ?
Notes : page 142.

NICHOLAS NYE

Thistle and darnel and dock grew there,
   And a bush, in the corner, of may,
On the orchard wall I used to sprawl
   In the blazing heat of the day ;
Half asleep and half awake,   5
   While the birds went twittering by,
And nobody there my lone to share
   But Nicholas Nye.

Nicholas Nye was lean and grey,
   Lame of a leg and old,   10
More than a score of donkey's years
   He had seen since he was foaled ;
He munched the thistles, purple and spiked,
   Would sometimes stoop and sigh,
And turn to his head, as if he said,   15
   " Poor Nicholas Nye ! "

Alone with his shadow he'd drowse in the meadow,
   Lazily swinging his tail,
At break of day he used to bray,
   Not much too hearty and hale ;   20
But a wonderful gumption was under his skin,
   And a clear calm light in his eye,
And once in a while, he'd smile—
   Would Nicholas Nye.

Seem to be smiling at me, he would,   25
   From his bush, in the corner, of may—
Bony and ownerless, widowed and worn,
   Knobble-kneed, lonely and grey ;
And over the grass would seem to pass
   'Neath the deep dark blue of the sky,   30
Something much better than words between me
   And Nicholas Nye.

But dusk would come in the apple boughs,
    The green of the glow-worm shine,
The birds in nest would crouch to rest,   35
    And home I'd trudge to mine ;
And there, in the moonlight, dark with dew,
    Asking not wherefore nor why,
Would brood like a ghost, and as still as a post,
    Old Nicholas Nye.   40

WALTER DE LA MARE
(*20th Century*)

widowed : *deprived of friends*

1. Picture the scene in stanza 1. Is there much movement in it ?

2. What references do you find to the weather ?

3. Had the poet " time to stand and stare " ?

4. In how many ways was the life the poet led similar to that led by Nicholas Nye ?

5. Compare the picture of the donkey given in lines 1-20 with that given in lines 21-40.

    (*a*) *How* do they differ ?

    (*b*) *Why* do they differ ?

6. What moved the poet to write this poem ? In which four lines does he answer this question most clearly ?

7. How will you read the poem ? How will you take the **short** lines that end the stanzas ?

8. In line 3 you will find an example of mid-rhyme—" wall ", " sprawl ". Find other examples in the poem.
   What additional peculiarity do you find in line 23 ?

Notes : page 143.

LONE DOG

I'm a lean dog, a keen dog, a wild dog, and lone ;
I'm a rough dog, a tough dog, hunting on my own ;
I'm a bad dog, a mad dog, teasing silly sheep ;
I love to sit and bay the moon, to keep fat souls from
    sleep.

I'll never be a lap dog, licking dirty feet,   5
A sleek dog, a meek dog, cringing for my meat,
Not for me the fireside, the well-filled plate,
But shut door, and sharp stone, and cuff, and kick, and
    hate.

Not for me the other dogs, running by my side,
Some have run a short while, but none of them would
    bide.   10
O mine is still the lone trail, the hard trail, the best,
Wide wind, and wild stars, and the hunger of the quest !

Irene R. McLeod
(20th Century)

1. Which of Lone Dog's adjectives in stanza 1 may be applied
   to Nicholas Nye ?
2. Is Lone Dog or Nicholas Nye the braver ?
3. Which of the two animals seems more real ? The donkey
   is silent, and the dog uses the pronoun " I ". But you will
   find other points of contrast.
4. We were given a very clear picture of Nicholas Nye's
   surroundings. Why are Lone Dog's left vague ?
5. Line 8 sounds " hateful ". Can you explain why ?
6. Read these lines aloud. The " beats " are marked for you.

    > *I'm a* **low** *dog, a* **slow** *dog, a* **fat** *dog, and* **old** ;
    > *I'm a* **fed** *dog, a* **led** *dog,* **walk**ing *where I'm* **told** ;
    > *I'm a* **puffed** *dog, a* **stuffed** *dog,* **eat**ing *cake and* **crumb** ;
    > *I* **love** *to* **think** *of* **meals** *I've* **had,** *and* **dream** *of* **meals**
    >   *to* **come.**

   Note that, though they describe a very different dog, those
   lines copy closely the rhythm of the first stanza of the
   poem. Compare the two stanzas, line by line, checking
   the end-rhymes, the mid-rhymes, the number of
   syllables, and the position of the " beats ".
7. (*a*) How will you read " Lone Dog " ?
   (*b*) How will you read " Low Dog ", question 6 ?

   Notes : page 144.

18

THE HUNT IS UP

The Hunt is up! The Hunt is up!
  And it is wellnigh day;
And Harry our King is gone hunting,
  To bring his deer to bay.

The East is bright with morning light;   5
  And darkness it is fled:
And the merry horn wakes up the Morn
  To leave his idle bed.

Behold, the skies with golden dyes
  Are glowing all around!   10
The grass is green, and so are the treen,
  All laughing at the sound!

The horses snort to be at the sport,
  The dogs are running free;
The woods rejoice at the merry noise   15
  Of Hey tantara tee ree!

The sun is glad to see us clad
  All in our lusty green;
And smiles in the sky, as he riseth high
  To see and to be seen.   20

Awake all men! I say again.
  Be merry, as you may;
For Harry our King is gone hunting,
  To bring his deer to bay.   WILLIAM GRAY
                       (c. 1530)

treen: *trees*   lusty: *cheerful*
tantara tee ree: *notes of the hunting horn*

1. How many " beats " are there in lines 1 and 3? How
   many in lines 2 and 4? Is each stanza formed in the
   same way as stanza 1?
2. In lines 5 and 7 we have examples of mid-rhyme—" bright ",
   " light "; " horn ", " Morn ". Find other examples in
   other stanzas.
   Why did the poet introduce mid-rhyme here?
3. What picture does this poem make you see?
4. How will you read the poem?

   Notes: page 145.

THE BATTLE OF QUIBERON BAY

In the Seven Years' War, 1756-1763, the British **navy** played a great part. By confining the French fleets to their harbours it deprived the French forces in India and America of home support, and enabled Clive and Wolfe to establish our overseas Empire. In 1759 the enemy fleets lay at Brest, on the Atlantic coast, and at Toulon, on the Mediterranean.

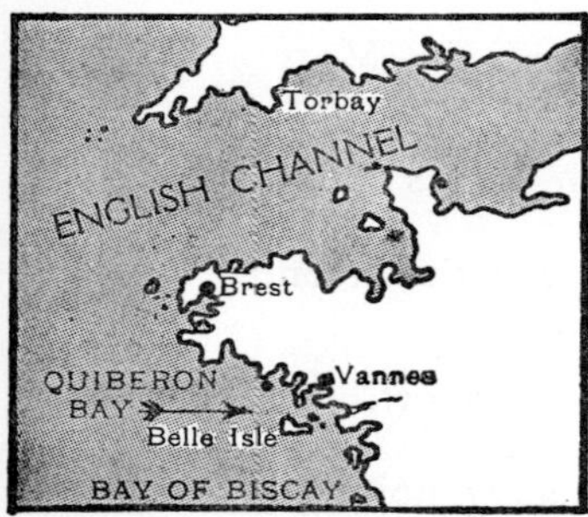

They were under orders to meet at Vannes, near Quiberon Bay, and convoy an army that lay there to an invasion of England. The Toulon fleet set out in August, and was shattered by Admiral Boscawen in Lagos Bay, on the coast of Portugal. At Brest, Admiral Hawke had kept watch in all weathers for six months, when, on 9th November, a westerly gale forced him to make for Torbay, in Devon, to refit. On 14th November he heard that Marshal de Conflans, the French admiral, had seized the opportunity to make for Vannes. On the 20th, in a heavy storm, the two fleets met outside Quiberon Bay. Hawke signalled " Line Abreast ", to bring his ships to-gether. Then came " Gen-eral Chase ", and " Line of Battle Ahead ". The French round-ed Belle Isle (see the map) at 2.30 p.m. and ran into the bay to find refuge, as they hoped, a-mong its rocks and shoals.

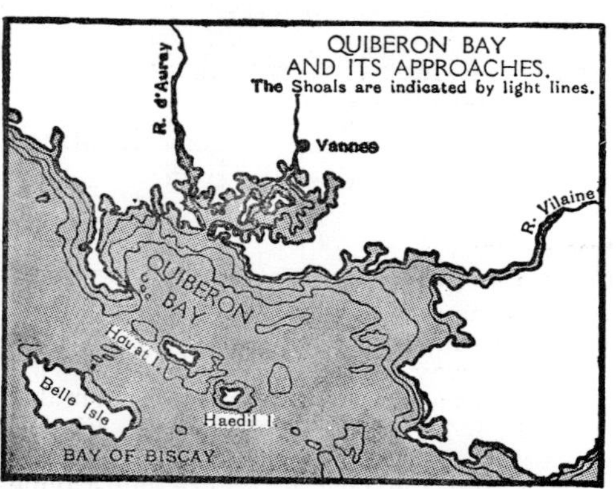

Hawke's pilot pointed out that further pursuit by a fleet
without knowledge of the waters was fraught with great
danger. " You have done your duty," said Hawke, " in this   45
remonstrance: you are now to obey my orders and lay me
alongside the French Admiral." The " swoop " went on. Of
the " twenty of the line", one struck her colours ; another
was sunk ; Conflans' flagship was forced to run ashore ;
four more were wrecked ; seven ran up the river Vilaine to   50
remain there for two years. The danger of a French
invasion was over.

HAWKE

In seventeen hundred and fifty-nine,
    When Hawke came swooping from the West,
The French King's Admiral with twenty of the line
    Was sailing forth, to sack us, out of Brest.
The ports of France were crowded, the quays of France
        a-hum   5
With thirty thousand soldiers marching to the drum,
For bragging time was over and fighting time was come
    When Hawke came swooping from the West.

'Twas long past noon of a wild November day
    When Hawke came swooping from the West ;   10
He heard the breakers thundering in Quiberon Bay,
    But he flew the flag for battle, line abreast.
Down upon the quicksands roaring out of sight
Fiercely beat the storm-wind, darkly fell the night,
But they took the foe for pilot and the cannon's glare   15
        for light
    When Hawke came swooping from the West.

The Frenchmen turned like a covey down the wind
  When Hawke came swooping from the West ;
One he sank with all hands, one he caught and pinned,
  And the shallows and the storm took the rest.   20
The guns that should have conquered us they rusted
      on the shore,
The men that would have mastered us they drummed
      and marched no more,
For England was England, and a mighty brood she bore
  When Hawke came swooping from the West.

SIR HENRY NEWBOLT

(20th Century)

1. Why does the poet speak of Hawke " swooping " ?
2. Which line makes you feel most proud to be the countryman
   of Hawke ?
3. Study the arrangement of the rhymes in the first stanza.
   Mark " nine " and its rhymes by *a*, " West " and its
   rhymes by *b*, " hum " and its rhymes by *c*. The rhyme
   arrangement, or rhyme-scheme, as it is usually called,
   is thus indicated by *a b a b c c c b.*
   Indicate in similar fashion the rhyme-schemes of stanza 2
   and stanza 3, and compare them with that of stanza 1.
4. We may think of each stanza as composed of three parts—
   lines 1-4, lines 5-7, line 8. How will you read each part ?
5. What did the prose introduction give you that you did not
   find in the poem ?
6. What did the poem give you that you did not find in the
   prose ?
7. Read again the prose, lines 32-47, and then this rhymed
   version :

   They rounded Belle Isle at 2.30 p.m.,
     And for refuge ran into the bay,
   For its rocks and its shoals were known only to them,
     And a great gale was blowing that day.
   Our pilot declared there was danger ahead
     For our ships, without knowledge to guide 'em.
   " 'Twas your duty to make this remonstrance," Hawke said ;
     " Mark the French, and lay me alongside 'em."

   Why are those lines inferior to stanza 2 of the poem ?

Notes : page 145.

29

A WET SHEET AND A FLOWING SEA

A wet sheet and a flowing sea,
  A wind that follows fast,
And fills the white and rustling sail,
  And bends the gallant mast !
And bends the gallant mast, my boys,   5
  While, like the eagle, free,
Away the good ship flies, and leaves
  Old England on the lee.

Oh for a soft and gentle wind !
  I heard a fair one cry ;   10
But give to me the snoring breeze,
  And white waves heaving high ;
The white waves heaving high, my lads,
  The good ship tight and free—
The world of waters is our home   15
  And merry men are we.

There's tempest in yon hornéd moon,
  And lightning in yon cloud ;
But hark the music, mariners !
  The wind is piping loud !   20
The wind is piping loud, my boys,
  The lightning flashes free—
The hollow oak our palace is,
  Our heritage, the sea.

CUNNINGHAM
(1784-1842)

sheet : *a rope fastened to the lower corner of a sail, or to a boom,
to keep the sail in place. With " a wind that follows fast",
the sheet is plunged in the sea, because the boom is thrust out,
over the water.*

1. Would this sailor have been glad to swoop with Hawke ?
2. This poem is written in three stanzas, each of eight lines.
    The lines have four beats and three beats alternately.
    The second line rhymes with the fourth and the sixth
    with the eighth.
    Is this a full description of the form of the poem ?
3. How will you read this poem ?
    Notes : page 147.

THE WRAGGLE TAGGLE GIPSIES

There were three gipsies a-come to the door,
And down-stairs ran the lady, O !
One sang high, and another sang low,
And another sang, Bonny, Bonny Biscay, O !

Then she pulled off her silk-finished gown,   5
And put on hose of leather, O !
The ragged, ragged rags that lay by the door ;
And she's gone with the wraggle taggle gipsies, O !

It was late at night when her lord came home,
Inquiring for his lady, O !   10
The servants, they could only say,
" She's gone with the wraggle taggle gipsies, O ! "

" Go, saddle to me my milk-white steed,
Go and fetch me my pony, O !
That I may ride and seek my bride,   15
Who is gone with the wraggle taggle gipsies, O ! "

O he rode far and he rode fast,
He rode through woods and copses, too,
Until he came to a cold open field ;
And she's there with the wraggle taggle gipsies, O !   20

" What makes you leave your house and land,
Your silk-finished gowns, and your money, O ?
What makes you leave your new-wedded lord,
To go with the wraggle taggle gipsies, O ? "

" What care I for my house and land,   25
My silk-finished gowns, and my money, O ?
What care I for my new-wedded lord ?
I'm gone with the wraggle taggle gipsies, O ! "

" Last night you slept in a goose-feather bed,
With sheets washed fine and whitely, O !
And to-night you'll sleep in a cold open field,
If you go with the wraggle taggle gipsies, O ! "

" What care I for your goose-feather bed,
With the sheets washed fine and whitely, O ?
To-night I shall sleep in a cold open field,
For I'm gone with the wraggle taggle gipsies, O ! "

ANONYMOUS

A poem like this, which tells an old story, and which was made long ago to be spoken, not read, is called a ballad. Ballads were handed down by word of mouth from generation to generation and were, many of them, very old before ever they were printed.

Other ballads in this book are " Johnnie Faa " (page 26) " Get Up and Bar the Door " (page 36) " Annan Water " (page 38) " Edom o' Gordon " (page 40) " The Wife of Usher's Well " (page 116).

1. Is this a sad poem ?

2. Has it a sad or a cheerful rhythm ?

3. What do you note regarding the rhymes ?

4. How will you read the poem ?

5. The stanza form is simple and very easy to imitate. Use it in a poem of your own making.

For additional questions see " Johnnie Faa ".

You will find another version of this story in " The Princess and the Gipsies ", a poem by Frances Cornford.

Notes : page 147.

JOHNNIE FAA

The gypsies came to our good lord's gate
  And oh, but they sang bonnie ;
They sang sae sweet, sae very very sweet,
  That down came our fair ladye ;

And she came tripping down the stair   5
  And a' her maids before her ;
But as soon as they saw her weel-faured face
  They cast the glamour o'er her.

" O come with me," says Johnnie Faa,
  " O come with me, my dearie ;   10
And I vow and I swear by the hilt of my sword
  That your lord shall nae mair come near ye."

Then she gied them the red red wine,
  And they gied her the ginger ;
But she gied him a far better thing—   15
  The gowd ring aff her finger.

" Gae tak' frae me this gay mantile
  And bring to me a plaidie ;
For if a' my kith and kin had sworn,
  I'd follow the gypsie laddie.   20

Yestreen I lay in a well-made bed
  Wi' a' my maids to attend me,
But this night I'll lie 'neath the moon and the stars
  Wi' an ash and an oak fornent me."

But when our good lord came hame at e'en,   25
  And speired for his fair ladye,
The ane she cried, and the other she replied,
  " She's awa' wi' the gypsie laddie."

" Gae saddle to me the black black steed,
  Gae saddle and mak' him ready :   30
Before that either I eat or I sleep
  I'll seek my ain fair ladye."

" Oh we were fifteen well-made men,
  Although we were na bonnie :
And we were a' put down for ane,   35
  A fair young wanton ladye."

ANONYMOUS

glamour : *spell, enchantment*   plaidie : *large shawl*

weel-faured : *well-favoured,*   fornent : *opposite, in front of*
  beautiful   speired : *inquired*

This ballad is said to be based on a legend that goes back
to the reign of James VI and I, and that may or may not be
true.   The gipsies, it is said, were taken and hanged, and the
lady, a Countess of Cassillis, in Ayrshire, was imprisoned for
life.   But it may be that the legend is based on the ballad.

1. Read again " The Wraggle Taggle Gipsies ", and make note
   of the stanzas in the one version which correspond to
   stanzas in the other.

2. The two poems do not always lay the same emphasis on
   the same facts.   What are the chief differences ?

3. Why did the ladies join the gipsies ?   Compare the reasons
   given in each poem.

4. Who speaks in stanza 9 of " Johnnie Faa " ?   Are the words
   a good ending to the poem ?

5. Which version of the story do you prefer ?

Notes : page 148.

SNATCHES FROM OLD SONGS

1. A CATCH

Here's a health unto His Majesty !
   With a fa, la, la, la, la !
Conversion to his enemies !
   With a fa, la, la, la, la !
And he that will not pledge his Health,   5
I wish him neither wit nor wealth,
Nor yet a rope to hang himself !
   With a fa, la, la, la, la !

From PLAYFORD's Catch That Catch Can (1667)

2. SWEET IDLENESS

I would not be a serving-man
   To carry the cloak-bag still,
Nor would I be a falconer
   The greedy hawks to fill ;
But I would be in a good house,   5
   And have a good master, too,
But I would eat and drink of the best,
   And no work would I do.

From The Knight of the Burning Pestle (1611)
BEAUMONT AND FLETCHER

In a catch, each singer sings the same melody. "A" begins alone. When he has reached a certain point, " B " takes up the words and melody from the beginning. Later, if there are parts enough, " C " and " D " join in, in similar fashion. A well-known catch is " London's Burning ".

1. Repeat each stanza until its rhythm is clear to you, and mark the " beats " in each line. How will you read line 2 of " A Catch " ?

2. Show by examination of " Sweet Idleness ", lines 1 and 5, that a word may carry accent in one line and lack it in another. How do you explain this ?

3. Will you read **each** snatch in the same way ?

Notes : page 149.

3. A CATCH

*Sung by two Satyrs to rouse two Sylvans, or wood-spirits,
asleep before the palace of Oberon*

Buz, quoth the blue fly,
    Hum, quoth the bee :
Buz and hum they cry,
    And so do we.
In his ear, in his nose ;   5
    Thus, do you see ?   *(They tickle them.)*
He ate the dormouse,
    Else it was he.

From *The Masque of Oberon* (1610)
BEN JONSON

4. THE URCHINS' DANCE

By the moon we sport and play,
With the night begins our day ;
As we frisk the dew doth fall :
Trip it, little urchins all !
Lightly as the little bee,   5
Two by two, and three by three ;
And about, about go we.

From THOMAS RAVENSCROFT'S *Brief Discourses* (1614)

satyrs : *Greek wood-gods*   urchins : *goblins*

Oberon : *King of Fairyland*

4. Explain lines 7 and 8 in No. 3.

5. Compare the rhythms of Nos. 3 and 4 with those of **Nos.**
   1 and 2 (page 28).

Notes : page 149.

A FANCY FROM FONTENELLE

De mémoires de Roses on n'a point vu mourir le Jardinier.

The Rose in the garden slipped her bud,
And she laughed in the pride of her youthful blood
As she thought of the Gardener standing by—
" He is old—so old ! And he soon must die ! "

The full Rose waxed in the warm June air,   5
And she spread and spread till her heart lay bare ;
And she laughed once more as she heard his tread—
" He is older now ! He will soon be dead ! "

But the breeze of the morning blew, and found
That the leaves of the blown Rose strewed the ground ; 10
And he came at noon, that Gardener old,
And he raked them gently under the mould.

And I wove the thing to a random rhyme,
For the Rose is Beauty, the Gardener, Time.

Austin Dobson (1840-1921)

fancy : *fanciful thought.*
The line means : No rose can remember the gardener
  dying. Fontenelle's actual words may be thus translated :
    If the roses which endure for but a day wrote histories,
    . . . they would say : We have always seen the same
  gardener ; in the memory of roses none has been seen but
  he ; he has always been the same as he is now ; assuredly
  he does not die like us, he does not even change.

1. If " the Rose is Beauty, the Gardener, Time ", what does
  the poet seem to say of all lovely things ?
2. (*a*) Is the triumph of Time over Beauty always so swift as
  it is here ? (*b*) Has the beauty of the Rose died ?
3. Has this poem a pleasing rhythm ? Compare it with
  that of " The Priest and the Mulberry Tree " (page 32).
4. How will you read this poem ?

  Notes : page 149.

SEPTEMBER

There are twelve months throughout the year,
  From January to December—
And the primest month of all the twelve
  Is the merry month of September!
    Then apples so red   5
    Hang overhead,
    And nuts ripe-brown
    Come showering down
In the bountiful days of September!

There are flowers enough in the summer-time,   10
  More flowers than I can remember—
But none with the purple, gold, and red
  That dye the flowers of September!
  The gorgeous flowers of September!
    And the sun looks through   15
    A clearer blue,
    And the moon at night
    Sheds a clearer light
On the beautiful flowers of September!

Mary Howitt
(1799-1888)

1. Is this poet happy or sad?

2. Why is September the " primest " month to her?

3. The following lines say the same things as the second stanza
of the poem.   Why are they less cheerful?

> *Summer's months have lovely flowers,*
>   *More than I can well recall.*
> *But for flowers of gorgeous hues*
>   *Autumn months are best of all.*
> *Through blue skies the sun shines bright,*
> *And the moon sheds clearer light.*

4. In reading this poem, how will you mark the short lines?

Notes : page 150.

THE PRIEST AND THE MULBERRY TREE

Did you hear of the curate who mounted his mare,
And merrily trotted along to the fair?
Of creature more tractable none ever heard;
In the height of her speed she would stop at a word;
And again with a word, when the curate said, " Hey ! " 5
She put forth her mettle and galloped away.

As near to the gates of the city he rode,
While the sun of September all brilliantly glowed,
The good priest discovered, with eyes of desire,
A mulberry tree in a hedge of wild briar; 10
On boughs long and lofty, in many a green shoot,
Hung, large, black, and glossy, the beautiful fruit.

The curate was hungry and thirsty to boot;
He shrank from the thorns, though he longed for the
    fruit;
With a word he arrested his courser's keen speed, 15
And he stood up erect on the back of his steed;
On the saddle he stood while the creature stood still,
And he gathered the fruit till he took his good fill.

" Sure never," he thought, " was a creature so rare,
So docile, so true, as my excellent mare; 20
Lo, here now I stand," and he gazed all around,
" As safe and as steady as if on the ground;
Yet how had it been, if some traveller this way,
Had, dreaming no mischief, but chanced to cry
    ' Hey ! ' "

He stood with his head in the mulberry tree, 25
And he spoke out aloud in his fond reverie.
At the sound of the word the good mare made a push,
And down went the priest in the wild briar bush.
He remembered too late, on his thorny, green bed,
Much that well may be thought, cannot wisely be said. 30

PEACOCK
(1785-1866)

1. If you were asked to illustrate this poem, which lines particularly would you choose for subjects of your sketches ?

2. Why is " tractable " a very important word in the description of the mare ?

3. This poem concludes with a proverb. Mention another that the curate might have remembered.

4. Are we to smile at the curate's mishap, or to feel sorry for him ?

5. Why has the poet chosen a curate for his victim, and not, say, a plough-boy ?

6. What in the first line gave you a hint that this might prove a cheerful poem ?

7. What other promises of cheerfulness were you given in the first stanza ?

8. Why did the poet decide to write this poem in a " ti-ti-tum " rhythm ?

9. How will you read this poem ?

Notes : page 151

ROUNDABOUTS AND SWINGS

It was early last September nigh to Framlin'am-on-
    Sea,
An' 'twas Fair-day come to-morrow, an' the time was
    after tea,
An' I met a painted caravan adown a dusty lane,
A Pharaoh with his waggons comin' jolt an' creak an'
    strain ;
A cheery cove an' sunburnt, bold o' eye and wrinkled
    up.   5
An' beside him on the splashboard sat a brindled
    tarrier pup,
An' a lurcher wise as Solomon an' lean as fiddle-
    strings
Was joggin' in the dust along 'is roundabouts and
    swings.

" Goo'-day," said 'e ; " Goo'-day," said I ; " an'
    'ow d'you find things go,
An' what's the chance o' millions when you runs a
    travellin' show ? "   10
" I find," said 'e, " things very much as 'ow I've
    always found,
For mostly they goes up and down or else goes round
    and round."
Said 'e, " The job's the very spit o' what it always were,
It's bread and bacon mostly when the dog don't catch a
    'are ;
But lookin' at it broad, an' while it ain't no merchant
    king's,   15
What's lost upon the roundabouts we pulls up on the
    swings ! "

" Goo' luck," said 'e ; " Goo' luck," said I ; " you've
    put it past a doubt ;
An' keep that lurcher on the road, the gamekeepers is
    out ; "
'E thumped upon the footboard an' 'e lumbered on again
To meet a gold-dust sunset down the owl-light in the
    lane ;
An' the moon she climbed the 'azels, while a night-
    jar seemed to spin
That Pharaoh's wisdom o'er again, 'is sooth of lose-
    and-win ;
For " up an' down an' round," said 'e, " goes all
    appointed things,
An' losses on the roundabouts means profits on the
    swings ! "

20

PATRICK CHALMERS (20th Century)

a Pharaoh : *a gipsy*   owl-light : *the dusk when owls begin to fly*
sooth of lose-and-win : *philosophy that loss and gain balance
each other*

1. Is the Pharaoh young, middle-aged, or old ?
2. Would " an early morn in April " have been as good a time
    to meet him and talk to him ?
3. What do you learn about the lurcher ?   Does line 7 imply
    that his master treats him badly ?
4. The night-jar has a monotonous, churring note. Show that
    lines 19-24 make a good conclusion to the poem.
5. Which of the poems you have already read does
    " Roundabouts and Swings " recall to you ?
6. This is a poem of evening.   Which poems of those you
    have read suggest to you other times of the day ?
7. Show that the poem should be read differently from " The
    Priest and the Mulberry Tree ".
    Compare with lines 9-12 this " ti-ti-tum " version of them :

*Then 'e bid me goo'-day, an' I bid 'im the same, an' I asked
    'ow 'e found things go,
An' what was the chance o' 'is makin' a pile by runnin' a
    travellin' show ;
An' 'e said as 'ow things were exactly the same with 'im now
    as 'e'd always found,
" For they goes up an' down as a rule," 'e went on, " if they 're
    not goin' round an' round."*

Notes : page 151.

35

GET UP AND BAR THE DOOR

It fell about the Martinmas time,
    And a gey time it was then,
When our goodwife got puddings to mak'
    And she's boil'd them in the pan.

The wind blew cauld frae north to south,   5
    And blew into the floor ;
Quoth our goodman to our goodwife,
    " Get up and bar the door."

" My hand is in my hussif-skip
    Goodman, as you may see ;   10
An it should na be barr'd this hundred year
    It s' no be barr'd for me."

They made a paction 'tween them twa,
    They made it firm and sure,
Whae'er should speak the foremost word   15
    Should rise and bar the door.

Then by there cam twa gentlemen,
    At twelve o'clock at night,
And they could neither see house nor hall,
    Nor coal nor candle-light.   20

" Now whether is this a rich man's house,
    Or whether is it a poor ? "
But ne'er a word would ane o' them speak,
    For barring o' the door.

And first they ate the white puddings,   25
    And then they ate the black ;
Though muckle thought the goodwife to hersel'
    Yet ne'er a word she spak.

Then said the ane unto the other,
    " Here, man, tak' you my knife ;   30
Do you tak' aff the auld man's beard,
    And I'll kiss the goodwife."

" But there's nae water in the house,
    And what shall we do then ? "
" What ails you at the pudding-bree,
    That boils into the pan ? "   35

O up then started our goodman,
    And an angry man was he :
" Will ye kiss my wife before my e'en,
    And scaud me wi' pudding-bree ? "   40

Then up and started our goodwife,
    Gied three skips on the floor :
" Goodman, you've spoken the foremost word,
    Get up and bar the door."

ANONYMOUS

Martinmas : *Feast of St. Martin, 11th November*
gey : *busy, bustling*   goodwife : *mistress of the house*   cauld : *cold*
goodman : *master of the house*   hussif-skip : *house-work*
it s' no be barred : *it shall not be barred*   paction : *bargain*
muckle : *much*   scaud : *scald*   gied : *gave*
pudding-bree : *water in which " puddings " have been boiled*

1. The story of this poem is told in two " chapters ". With
   which stanza does Chapter 2 begin ?
2. The ballad-maker always tells his story briefly, giving only
   the main points in it. Find four places in this ballad
   where a writer who wished to give fuller details might
   insert stanzas.
3. You will observe that the poem is composed of stanzas of
   four lines, lines 1 and 3 having each four " beats ", lines 2
   and 4, each three. The second and fourth lines rhyme.

   > *The* **wind** *blew* **cauld** *frae* **north** *to* **south,**
   >   *And* **blew** *into the* **floor ;**
   >   Quoth **our** *goodman to* **our** *goodwife,*
   >   " *Get* **up** *and* **bar** *the* **door."**

   This is the regular ballad stanza.
   Make a stanza of your own to link up stanzas 4 and 5, or
   stanzas 6 and 7. The best way to understand rhythm is
   to fit words to it.
4. Who speaks in lines 21, 22 ? To whom is he speaking ?
5. Is it right that the goodwife should triumph ?
6. With which, " The Wraggle Taggle Gipsies " or " Johnnie
   Faa ", has this ballad more in common ?
   Notes : page 152.

37

ANNAN WATER

" Annan Water's running deep,
   And my love Annie's wondrous bonnie ;
And I am laith she should wet her feet,
   Because I lo'e her best of ony."

He has loupen on his bonnie gray,   5
   He rade the right gait and the ready ;
I trow he would neither stent nor stay,
   For he was seeking his bonnie lady.

Oh he has ridden ower field and fell,
   Through moor and moss and mony a mire ;   10
His spurs o' steel were sair to bide
   And from her fore-feet flew the fire,

" My bonnie gray, now play your part.
   Gin ye be the steed that wins my dearie,
Wi' corn and hay you'll be fed for aye,   15
   And never spur shall make you weary."

The gray was a mare, and a right good mare,
   But when she wan the Annan Water,
She could na ha'e ridden a furlong mair,
   Had a thousand merks been wadded at her.   20

" O boatman, boatman, put off your boat,
   Put off your boat for gowden money :
I cross the drumlie stream this night,
   Or never mair I see my honey.

" Oh I was sworn so late yestreen,   25
   And not by ae aith, but by many."
But for a' the gowd in fair Scotland
   He daurna take him through to Annie.

The side was stey, and the bottom deep,
   Frae bank to brae the water pouring ;   30
And the bonnie gray mare, she swat for fear,
   For she heard the water-kelpie roaring.

He has ta'en the ford at the stream-tail.
    I wot she swam baith strong and steady ;
But the stream was broad and her strength did fail,   35
    And he never saw his bonnie lady.

ANONYMOUS

gait : *way*

stent : *stop*

merk : *old Scots silver coin*

wadded : *wagered*

drumlie : *dark and troubled*

daurna : *dare not*

stey : *steep*

water-kelpie : *river demon that exults in the deaths of men*

stream-tail : *the end of a current, where the water is calmer*

1. Who speaks in lines 1-4, 13-16, 21-26 ?

2. Why are the speeches introduced so abruptly ?

3. What does the ballad tell of the appearance of the hero and his lady ?

4. In which was the maker of the ballad more interested, story or description ?

5. Why was the hero determined upon crossing the river that night ?

6. Which stanza gives the best impression of the difficulties of the road ?   Pick out the descriptive words in it.

7. What qualities in the hero do you admire ?

8. Which stanza first told you that this ballad was to end sadly ?

9. The story is told simply.   The teller makes no attempt to draw our tears.   Why, then, does he move us so deeply ?

Notes : page 153.

EDOM O' GORDON

It fell about the Martinmas,
  When the wind blew shrill and cauld,
Said Edom o' Gordon to his men,
  " We maun draw to a hauld.

" And whatna hauld sall we draw to, 5
  My merry men and me ?
We will gae to the House o' the Rodes,
  To see that fair ladye."

The lady stood on her castle wa', 10
  Beheld baith dale and down ;
There she was ware of a host of men
  Cam riding towards the toun.

" O see ye not, my merry men a',
  O see ye not what I see ?
Methinks I see a host of men ; 15
  I marvel wha they be."

She had nae sooner buskit hersei,
  And putten on her gown,
Till Edom o' Gordon and his men
  Were round about the toun. 20

They had nae sooner supper set,
  Nae sooner said the grace,
Till Edom o' Gordon and his men
  Were light about the place.

The lady ran up to her tower-head, 25
  Sae fast as she could hie,
To see if by her fair speeches
  She could wi' him agree.

Gie owre your house, ye lady fair,
   Gie owre your house to me ;
Or I sall brenn yoursel therein,
   But and your babies three."

" I winna gie owre, ye fals Gordon,
   To nae sic traitor as ye ;
Though ye should brenn mysel therein,
   But and my babies three.

" Now reach my pistol, Glaud, my man,
   And charge ye weel my gun ;
For, but an I pierce that bluidy butcher,
   My babes, we been undone ! "

She stood upon her castle wa',
   And let twa bullets flee :
She miss'd that bluidy butcher's heart,
   And only razed his knee.

" Set fire to the house ! " quo' fals Gordon,
   A' wud wi' dule and ire :
" Fals lady, ye sall rue that shot
   As ye brenn in the fire ! "

" Wae worth, wae worth ye, Jock, my man !
   I paid ye weel your fee ;
Why pu' ye out the grund-wa' stane,
   Lets in the reek to me ?

" And e'en wae worth ye, Jock, my man !
   I paid ye weel your hire ;
Why pu' ye out the grund-wa' stane,
   To me lets in the fire ? "

" Ye paid me weel my hire, lady,
   Ye paid me weel my fee :
But now I'm Edom o' Gordon's man—
   Maun either do or dee."

30
35
40
45
50
55
60

41

O then outspake her youngest son,
  Sat on the nurse's knee :
Says, " Mither dear, gie owre this house,
  For the reek it smothers me."

" I wad gie a' my gowd, my bairn,   65
  Sae wad I a' my fee,
For ae blast o' the western wind,
  To blaw the reek frae thee."

O then outspake her dochter dear—
  She was baith jimp and sma' :   70
" O row me in a pair o' sheets,
  And tow me owre the wa' ! "

They row'd her in a pair o' sheets,
  And tow'd her owre the wa' ;
But on the point o' Gordon's spear   75
  She gat a deadly fa'.

O bonnie, bonnie was her mouth,
  And cherry were her cheeks,
And clear, clear was her yellow hair,
  Whereon the red blood dreips.   80

Then wi' his spear he turn'd her owre ;
  O gin her face was wan !
He said, " Ye are the first that e'er
  I wish'd alive again."

He turn'd her owre and owre again ;   85
  O gin her skin was white !
" I might hae spared that bonnie face
  To hae been some man's delight.

" Busk and boun, my merry men a',
  For ill dooms I do guess ;   90
I canna look in that bonnie face
  As it lies on the grass."

" Wha looks to freits, my master dear,
    It's freits will follow them ;
Let it ne'er be said that Edom o' Gordon   95
    Was daunted by a dame."

But when the lady saw the fire
    Come flaming owre her head,
She wept, and kiss'd her children twain,
    Says, " Bairns, we been but dead."   100

The Gordon then his bugle blew,
    And said, " Awa', awa' !
This House o' the Rodes is a' in a flame ;
    I hauld it time to ga'."

O then he spied her ain dear lord,   105
    As he cam owre the lea.
He saw his castle a' in a lowe,
    As far as he could see.

" Put on, put on, my wighty men,
    Sae fast as ye can drie !   110
For he that's hindmost o' the thrang
    Sall ne'er get good o' me."

Then some they rade, and some they ran,
    Out ower the grass and bent ;
But ere the foremost could win up,   115
    Baith lady and babes were brent.

And after the Gordon he is gane,
    Sae fast as he might drie ;
And soon i' the Gordon's foul heart's blude
    He's wroken his dear lady.   120

And mony were the mudie men
    Lay gasping on the green ;
And mony were the fair ladies
    Were lemanless at hame.

And mony were the mudie men
  Lay gasping on the green ;
For o' fifty men the Gordon brocht
  There were but five gaed hame.

ANONYMOUS

Martinmas : 11th November
draw to a hauld : make for a
  house
toun : dwelling
buskit : attired
gie owre : give up
brenn : burn
wud : mad
dule : grief, pain
wae worth ye : may ill befall
  you
grund-wa' : ground-wall
fee : wages, wealth

reek : smoke
jimp : slender, neat
row : roll, wrap
busk and boun : make ready
  to go
freits : ill omens
lowe : flame
wighty : stalwart
drie : endure
win up : arrive
wroken : avenged
mudie : bold
lemanless : loverless

In 1571 Adam, or Edom, Gordon upheld the cause of Queen Mary in the north of Scotland. The Master of Forbes was commissioned by the ruling Protestant party to take the field against him. During the fighting Towie Castle, in Aberdeenshire, was burned, not by Gordon himself, but by a Captain Ker, a soldier in his service. Lady Forbes, her children, and her servants, twenty-seven persons in all, died in the flames. The ballad makes Gordon responsible for the deed of his officer ; and southern reciters have transferred the scene of it from Aberdeenshire to Berwickshire. The House o' the Rodes was a stronghold near Duns, where the Gordons held lands at one time.

1. With whom does the maker of the ballad sympathise ?

2. You have been told that ballads use adjectives sparingly. See " Annan Water ", and particularly notes 4, 8, and 9 (page 154). Why are adjectives so numerous in lines 70, 77-80, 86 of " Edom o' Gordon " ?

3. Is the ballad right in making Gordon speak as he does in lines 83-4, and 87-92 ?

4. Some versions of the poem omit the last three stanzas. Which ending do you prefer ?

Notes : page 155.

44

A SONG

The feathers of the willow
Are half of them grown yellow
  Above the swelling stream ;
And ragged are the bushes,
And rusty now the rushes,
  And wild the clouded gleam.

The thistle now is older,
His stalk begins to moulder,
  His head is white as snow ;
The branches all are barer,
The linnet's song is rarer,
  The robin pipeth now.

RICHARD WATSON DIXON
(1833-1900)

NOVEMBER DAYS

I love the fitful gust that shakes
  The casement all the day,
And from the glossy elm-tree takes
  The faded leaves away,
Twirling them by the window pane
With thousand others down the lane.

I love to see the shaking twig
  Dance till the shut of eve,
The sparrow on the cottage rig,
  Whose chirp would make believe
That Spring was just now flirting by
In Summer's lap with flowers to lie.

45

I love to see the cottage smoke
    Curl upwards through the trees,
The pigeons nestled round the cote   15
    On November days like these ;
The cock upon the dunghill crowing,
The mill sails on the heath a-going.

The feather from the raven's breast
    Falls on the stubble lea,   20
The acorns near the old crow's nest
    Drop pattering down the tree ;
The grunting pigs, that wait for all,
Scramble and hurry where they fall.

CLARE
(1793-1864)

rig : *ridge*　　　　　　　　flirting : *dancing gaily*

1. Though Dixon and Clare have the same theme—the fading
    year—the scenes they describe differ greatly. What does
    each poem make you see ? In which do you feel more
    strongly that summer is over ?

2. In which scene—Dixon's or Clare's—is there more move-
    ment ?

3. How do the autumn sounds referred to in " A Song " differ
    from those of " November Days " ?

4. Clare tells us he is happy in the season he describes. What
    does he most delight in ? Is Dixon happy or unhappy ?

5. Which poet presents the truer picture ? Which the more
    pleasing ?

6. Each poet writes in short lines, in a six-line stanza. Why is
    it that Dixon's poem sounds less lively than Clare's ?

7. You have been asked to note the contrasts presented by
    those poems. How will you bring out the contrasts in
    your reading ?

Notes : page 155.

46

LATE AUTUMN

The boy called to his team
  And with blue-glancing share
Turned up the rape and turnip
  With yellow charlock to spare.

The long lean thistles stood   5
  Like beggars ragged and blind,
Half their white silken locks
  Blown away in the wind.

But I thought not once of winter
  Or summer that was past   10
Till I saw that slant-legged robin
  With autumn on his chest.

ANDREW YOUNG
(20th Century)

share : *plough-share*   charlock : *wild mustard*
rape : *low-growing plant, the leaves of which are food for sheep*

WINTER

A widow bird sate mourning for her love
  Upon a wintry bough ;
The frozen wind crept on above,
  The freezing stream below.

There was no leaf upon the forest bare,   5
  No flower upon the ground,
And little motion in the air
  Except the mill-wheel's sound.

SHELLEY
(1792-1822)

1. Read again " A Song " (page 45). Point out the resemblances you detect between it and " Late Autumn ".
2. Which of the pictures in " Late Autumn " do you like best ?
3. Why was it only the robin that made the poet think of
   winter ?
4. How most of all does Shelley make you feel the desolation
   of winter ?
5. Do you feel that those poems are too short ?

   Notes : page 157.

THE STORM-BLAST

And now the Storm-blast came, and he
   Was tyrannous and strong :
He struck with his o'ertaking wings,
   And chased us south along.

With sloping masts and dipping prow,   5
As who, pursued with yell and blow,
Still treads the shadow of his foe,
   And forward bends his head,
The ship drove fast, loud roared the blast,
   And southward aye we fled.   10

From *The Rime of the Ancient Mariner*
COLERIDGE (1772-1834)

SEA-WEED

When descends on the Atlantic
The gigantic
   Storm-wind of the Equinox,
Landward in his wrath he scourges
The toiling surges,   5
   Laden with sea-weed from the rocks

From Bermuda's reefs ; from edges
Of sunken ledges,
   In some far-off, bright Azore ;
From Bahama, and the dashing,   10
Silver-flashing
   Surges of San Salvador ;

From the tumbling surf, that buries
The Orkneyan skerries,
   Answering the hoarse Hebrides ;   15

And from wrecks of ships, and drifting
Spars, uplifting
  On the desolate, rainy seas :

Ever drifting, drifting, drifting,
On the shifting   20
  Currents of the restless main ;
Till in sheltered coves and reaches
Of sandy beaches,
  All have found repose again.

LONGFELLOW
(1807-1882)

Equinox : *time of the year when day and night are equal, thought to be a time of storms*
skerries : *rocky islets*

1. Why does Coleridge call the Storm-blast " tyrannous " ?
2. What third adjective (in addition to " tyrannous " and " strong ") is suggested to you by lines 3-10 as a good description of the Storm-blast ?
3. What picture do you see in lines 6-8 of Coleridge's poem ?
4. How has the poet made us feel (*a*) the speed, and (*b*) the fury of the blast ?
5. Study a map of the Atlantic Ocean. Why has Longfellow chosen places so far apart ? Is " gigantic " a suitable word to describe the Storm-wind ?
6. How many sentences are there in " Sea-weed " ? What effect has the poet produced by writing it in this form ?
7. If you were asked to form a poem from two, only, of the four stanzas given here, which must you retain ?
8. What would we have lost if the poem had consisted of these two stanzas only ?
9. Name the four words that do most to convey the storm-sound in the first stanza.
10. Read this shorter version of the first stanza :
    > *When descends on the Atlantic*
    >   *The Storm-wind of the Equinox,*
    > *Landward in his wrath he scourges*
    >   *Waves with sea-weed from the rocks.*

    It retains most of the meaning. What has it lost ?
11. One stanza of " Sea-weed " must not be read in the same way as the others. Which is it ?
12. Describe the pictures you would make of the Storm-blast and the Storm-wind.
13. What will you try to make your hearer feel when you read the poems once more aloud ?
    Notes : page 158.

THE WITCHES' CHARM

The owl is abroad, the bat, and the toad,
   And so is the cat-a-mountain ;
The ant and the mole sit both in a hole,
   And the frog peeps out o' the fountain ;
The dogs they do bay, and the timbrels play,   5
   The spindle is now a-turning ;
The moon it is red, and the stars are fled,
   But all the sky is a-burning.
The ditch is made, and our nails the spade,
With pictures full, of wax and of wool ;   10
Their livers I stick with needles quick ;
There lacks but the blood, to make up the flood.
   Quickly, Dame, then bring your part in ;
   Spur, spur upon Little Martin :
   Merrily, merrily make him sail,   15
   A worm in his mouth, and a thorn in his tail,
   Fire above, and fire below,
With a whip in your hand to make him go.

From *The Masque of the Queens* (1609)
BEN JONSON (1573-1637)

Read the note on page 159.

The living things mentioned in lines 1-5 are creatures of ill-omen. Timbrels, spindles, ditches dug by the nails, images of wax and wool are part of the stock-in-trade of witchcraft. Little Martin is " a great goat upon whom they ride to their meetings ".

1. In what colours would you paint the scene described in lines 1-8 ?

2. In addition to making you see, what do those same lines make you feel ?

3. A dance of witches would be wild and excited. See the note, page 159.
   (a) Why may the poet have used mid-rhyme so freely ?
   (b) Why may he have written the poem in three parts (lines 1-8, 9-12, 13-18) each with a rhythm of its own ?

Notes : page 159.

UP IN THE MORNING EARLY

Up in the morning 's no for me,
  Up in the morning early ;
When a' the hills are cover'd wi' snaw,
  I'm sure it 's winter fairly.

Cauld blaws the wind frae east to west,   5
  The drift is driving sairly ;
Sae loud and shrill 's I hear the blast,
  I'm sure it 's winter fairly.

The birds sit chittering in the thorn,
  A' day they fare but sparely ;   10
And lang 's the night frae e'en to morn,
  I'm sure it 's winter fairly.

Up in the morning 's no for me,
  Up in the morning early ;
When a' the hills are cover'd wi' snaw,   15
  I'm sure it 's winter fairly.

BURNS
(1759-1796)

drift : *driving snow*   chittering : *shivering*

1. In which single line do you feel the cold most ?

2. Which is the more wintry, stanza 1, or stanza 2 ?

3. What will you try to bring out in your reading of the poem ?

4. Will you read the fourth stanza in the same way as you
  read the first ?

Notes : page 160.

51

THE FALLOW DEER AT THE LONELY HOUSE

One without looks in to-night
  Through the curtain-chink
From the sheet of glistening white ;
One without looks in to-night
  As we sit and think   5
  By the fender-brink.

We do not discern those eyes
  Watching in the snow ;
Lit by lamps of rosy dyes
We do not discern those eyes   10
  Wondering, aglow,
  Fourfooted, tiptoe.

THOMAS HARDY
(*20th Century*)

1. Can you tell from the poem, itself, that the house is lonely ?

2. Which word tells us most about the people in the house ?

3. Which word tells us most about the deer ?

4. Picture the scenes, as they appear (*a*) to one in the house ;
(*b*) to one out of doors. What have they in common ?

5. Lines 11, 12. Why does the poet apply those words to
" eyes " ?

6. Line 1. Why *One without looks in to-night,* and not *A
fallow deer looks in to-night ?*

7. Read again " Winter " (page 47). Compare the methods
chosen by Shelley and Hardy to make us feel the stillness of the scenes they describe.

8. What would be the effect of omitting line 4 ?

9. How will you read this poem ?

   Notes : page 161.

MILK FOR THE CAT

When the tea is brought at five o'clock,
And all the neat curtains are drawn with care,
The little black cat with bright green eyes
Is suddenly purring there.

At first she pretends, having nothing to do,   5
She has come in merely to blink by the grate,
But, though tea may be late or the milk may be sour,
She is never late.

And presently her agate eyes
Take a soft, large, milky haze,   10
And her independent casual glance
Becomes a stiff, hard gaze.

Then she stamps her claws or lifts her ears,
Or twists her tail and begins to stir,
Till suddenly all her lithe body becomes   15
One breathing, trembling purr.

The children eat and wriggle and laugh ;
The two old ladies stroke their silk :
But the cat is grown small and thin with desire,
Transformed to a creeping lust for milk.   20

The white saucer like some full moon descends
At last from the clouds of the table above ;
She sighs and dreams and thrills and glows,
Transfigured with love.

She nestles over the shining rim,   25
Buries her chin in the creamy sea ;
Her tail hangs loose ; each drowsy paw
Is doubled under each bending knee.

A long, dim ecstasy holds her life ;
Her world is an infinite shapeless white,   30
Till her tongue has curled the last holy drop,
Then she sinks back into the night,

Draws and dips her body to heap
Her sleepy nerves in the great arm-chair,
Lies defeated and buried deep   35
Three or four hours unconscious there.

HAROLD MONRO
(20th Century)

agate : *a clear, hard stone*
independent : *unattached*
casual : *unconcerned, off-hand*
lithe : *supple*
transformed : *changed in disposition*
lust : *strong desire*

transfigured : *changed in appearance*
ecstasy : *rapture, trance of joy*
infinite : *boundless*
defeated : *overcome, overwhelmed*

1. What is the season of the year?
2. What do you learn of the house and its inmates?
3. Compare this house with the Lonely House (page 52).
4. Lines 17-18. Why does the poet give those two lines to the ladies and the children?
5. Lines 21-22. Explain "full moon" and "clouds".
6. Lines 25-31. Would you say the cat is "greedy"?
7. Lines 32-35. Explain "night", "draws", "dips", "heap", "defeated".
8. Compare as pictures of animals, "Milk for the Cat", "Nicholas Nye" (page 16) "Lone Dog" (page 18) "The Fallow Deer at the Lonely House" (page 52).
9. Here is an attempt to describe the behaviour of the cat in ordinary prose :

   In some marvellous way the little black cat knows the hour for tea. At once she appears, as if from nowhere, and sits by the fire, in a sleepy way, as though tea meant nothing to her. But she cannot preserve this mood of indifference for long. Her eyes grow soft with longing and are fixed steadily on the tea-table. Then she twitches, and stirs, and purrs excitedly, goes tense and taut in her eagerness. A saucer is filled with milk from the table and put before her. She nestles above it, buries her chin in the contents, and gives herself up to delight. She is aware of nothing but the milk before her. It is the whole world to her. Only when she has taken the last drop, does she relax. Her craving is satisfied. She is at peace, and for hours she lies, overwhelmed in sleep, in the great chair by the fire.

   What differences do you find between the prose and the poetry?

Notes : page 162.

ODE TO THE NORTH-EAST WIND

Welcome, wild North-easter !
  Shame it is to see
Odes to every zephyr,
  Ne'er a verse to thee.
Welcome, black North-easter !   5
  O'er the German foam,
O'er the Danish moorlands,
  From thy frozen home.
Tired we are of summer,
  Tired of gaudy glare,   10
Showers soft and steaming,
  Hot and breathless air.
Tired of listless dreaming,
  Through the lazy day :
Jovial wind of winter,   15
  Turn us out to play !
Sweep the golden reed-beds ;
  Crisp the lazy dyke ;
Hunger into madness
  Every plunging pike.   20
Fill the lake with wild-fowl ;
  Fill the marsh with snipe ;
While on dreary moorlands
  Lonely curlew pipe.
Through the black fir-forest   25
  Thunder harsh and dry,
Shattering down the snow-flakes
  Off the curdled sky.
Hark ! The brave North-easter !
  Breast-high lies the scent,   30
On by holt and headland,
  Over heath and bent.

Chime, ye dappled darlings,
   Through the sleet and snow :
Who can over-ride you ?   35
   Let the horses go !
Chime, ye dappled darlings,
   Down the roaring blast ;
You shall see a fox die
   Ere an hour be past.   40
Go ! and rest to-morrow,
   Hunting in your dreams,
While our skates are ringing
   O'er the frozen streams.
Let the luscious South-wind   45
   Breathe in lover's sighs,
While the lazy gallants
   Bask in ladies' eyes.
What does he but soften
   Heart alike and pen ?   50
'Tis the hard grey weather
   Breeds hard English men.
What 's the soft South-wester ?
   'Tis the ladies' breeze,
Bringing home their true-loves   55
   Out of all the seas :
But the black North-easter,
   Through the snowstorm hurled,
Drives our English hearts of oak
   Seaward round the world.   60
Come, as came our fathers,
   Heralded by thee,
Conquering from the eastward,
   Lords by land and sea.

Come ; and strong within us
  Stir the Viking's blood ;
Bracing brain and sinew ;
  Blow, thou wind of God !

CHARLES KINGSLEY
(1819-1875)

zephyr : *light breeze* dyke : *ditch*

crisp : *ripple* dappled darlings : *foxhounds*

Who can override you ? *With the scent breast-high, the hounds run strongly, and the horsemen have no fear of riding into them.*

1. Lines 5-8, and 52-64. Study a map of Western Europe.

2. In which part of the country does the poet choose to sport with the North-easter ?

3. What sports are referred to in lines 17-44 ?
   What qualities do they call for ?

4. In which lines do you best hear the wind ?

5. Why has this poem been written in one piece, and not in stanzas ?

6. Why does the poet conclude by calling the North-easter " thou wind of God " ?

7. How will you read this poem ? What changes in tone, pace, etc., will you make in the course of your reading ?

Notes : page 164.

FOLLOW, OH FOLLOW !

This passage comes from "Maid Marian", a novel about the days of Robin Hood.

The marriage of the Earl of Locksley (Robin Hood) and Matilda, or Marian, daughter of the Baron of Arlingford, should have taken place on the day previous to that of which we are to read. But in the middle of the actual ceremony an armed troop had arrived at the Abbey of Rubygill, had forbidden the marriage in the King's name, and denounced the bridegroom as a traitor. The Earl and his followers had made good their escape in the mêlée, and Matilda had returned to her father's castle. This morning the King's officer has called upon the Baron of Arlingford to apologise for his intervention at Rubygill. He has been guided on his journey by a staunch admirer of Matilda, Brother Michael, a keen woodsman, so expert with the quarter-staff that he can be no other than Friar Tuck. Knight and friar have been ushered into a stately apartment where they have found the Baron alone, " flourishing an enormous carving-knife over a brother baron—of beef ". He is, as we shall discover, rather an irascible baron, so angry, indeed, with both parties, Robin's and the King's, that he does not know on which to vent his wrath. In the midst of the conversation Matilda trips into the apartment " in a dress of forest green, with a small quiver by her side, and a bow and arrow in her hand ".

baron of beef : *a double sirloin*

With a smile of recognition to the friar, and a courtesy to the stranger knight, she approached the baron and said, " You are late at your breakfast, father."

" I am not at breakfast," said the baron. " I have been at supper : my last night's supper ; for I had 5 none."

" I am sorry," said Matilda, " you should have gone to bed supperless."

" I did not go to bed supperless," said the baron : " I did not go to bed at all : and what are you doing with 10 that green dress and that bow and arrow ? "

" I am going a-hunting," said Matilda.

" A-hunting ! " said the baron. " What, I warrant you, to meet with the earl, and slip your neck into the same noose ? "
15

" No," said Matilda : " I am not going out of our own
woods to-day."

" How do I know that ? " said the baron. " What
surety have I of that ? "

" Here is the friar," said Matilda. " He will be
surety."

" Not he," said the baron : " he will undertake nothing
but where the devil is a party concerned."

" Yes, I will," said the friar : " I will undertake
anything for the lady Matilda."

" No matter for that," said the baron : " she shall not
go hunting to-day."

" Why, father," said Matilda, " if you coop me up here
in this odious castle, I shall pine and die like a lonely swan
on a pool."

" No," said the baron, " the lonely swan does not die
on the pool. If there be a river at hand, she flies to the
river, and finds her a mate ; and so shall not you."

" But," said Matilda, " you may send with me any, or as
many, of your grooms as you will."

" My grooms," said the baron, " are all false knaves.
There is not a rascal among them but loves you better
than me. Villains that I feed and clothe."

" Surely," said Matilda, " it is not villainy to love me :
if it be, I should be sorry my father were an honest man."
The baron relaxed his muscles into a smile. " Or my
lover either," added Matilda. The baron looked grim
again.

They discuss, for a time, the forest laws, the blessing of a roof
over one's head, life in the green-wood.

" Well, father," said Matilda, " I must go to the
woods."

" Must you ? " said the baron : " I say you must not."

" But I am going," said Matilda.

" But I will have up the drawbridge," said the baron.

" But I will swim the moat," said Matilda.

"But I will secure the gates," said the baron.   50
"But I will leap from the battlement," said Matilda.
"But I will lock you in an upper chamber," said the
baron
"But I will shred the tapestry," said Matilda, "and
let myself down."   55
"But I will lock you in a turret," said the baron,
"where you shall only see light through a loophole."
"But through that loophole," said Matilda, "will I
take my flight, like a young eagle from its aerie: and,
father, while I go out freely, I will return willingly: 60
but if once I slip out through a loophole."—She paused
a moment, then added, singing:

> "The love that follows fain
>   Will never its faith betray:
> But the faith that is held in a chain   65
> Will never be found again,
>   If a single link give way."

The melody acted irresistibly on the harmonious
propensities of the friar, who accordingly sang in his
turn: 70

> "For hark! hark! hark!
> The dog doth bark,
>   That watches the wild deer's lair,
> The hunter awakes at the peep of the dawn,
> But the lair is empty, the deer it is gone,   75
>   And the hunter knows not where."

Matilda and the friar then sang together:

> "Then follow, oh follow! the hounds do cry:
> The red sun flames in the eastern sky:
>   The stag bounds over the hollow.   80
> He that lingers in spirit, or loiters in hall,
> Shall see us no more till the evening fall,
> And no voice but the echo shall answer his call:
>   Then follow, oh follow, follow!
>   Follow, oh follow, follow!"   85

"... A hunting friar, truly!" said the baron. "Who ever heard before of a hunting friar? A profane, roaring, bawling, bumper-bibbing, neck-breaking, catch-singing friar?"

"Under favour, bold baron," said the friar; but he was in his singing vein; and he could not go on in plain unmusical prose. He therefore sang in a new tune:

"Though I be now a grey, grey friar,
    Yet I was once a hale young knight:
The cry of my dogs was the only choir
    In which my spirit did take delight.

"Little I recked of matin bell,
    But drowned its toll with my clanging horn:
And the only beads I loved to tell
    Were the beads of dew on the spangled thorn."

The baron was going to storm, but the friar paused, and Matilda sang in repetition:

"Little I reck of matin bell,
    But drown its toll with my clanging horn:
And the only beads I love to tell
    Are the beads of dew on the spangled thorn."

And then she and the friar sang the four lines together, and rang the changes upon them alternately.

"Little I reck of matin bell,"

sang the friar.

"A precious friar," said the baron.

"But drown its toll with my clanging horn,"

said Matilda.

"More shame for you," said the baron.

"And the only beads I love to tell
    Are the beads of dew on the spangled thorn,"

sang Matilda and the friar together.

"Penitent and confessor," said the baron: "a hopeful pair, truly."

The friar went on:

> " An archer keen I was withal,
>   As ever did lean on greenwood tree;
> And could make the fleetest roebuck fall,
>   A good three hundred yards from me.

> " Though changeful time, with hand severe,   125
>   Has made me now these joys forego,
> Yet my heart bounds whene'er I hear
>   Yoicks! hark away! and tally ho!"

Matilda chimed in as before.

" Are you mad?" said the baron. " Are you insane? 130
Are you possessed? What do you mean? What do you
both mean?"

" Yoicks! hark away! and tally ho!"

roared the friar.

The baron's pent-up wrath had accumulated like the 135
waters above the dam of an overshot mill. The pond-head
of his passion being now filled to the utmost limit of its
capacity, and beginning to overflow in the quivering of
his lips and the flashing of his eyes, he pulled up all
the flash-boards at once, and gave loose to the full torrent 140
of his indignation, by seizing, like furious Ajax, not a
massy stone more than two modern men could raise,
but a vast dish of beef, more than fifty ancient yeomen
could eat, and whirled it like a coit *in terrorem* over the
head of the friar, to the extremity of the apartment,   145

> Where it on oaken floor did settle,
> With mighty din of ponderous metal.

" Nay, father," said Matilda, taking the baron's hand,
" do not harm the friar: he means not to offend you.
My gaiety never before displeased you. Least of all 150
should it do so now, when I have need of all my spirits
to outweigh the severity of my fortune."

As she spoke the last words, tears started into her
eyes, which, as if ashamed of the involuntary betraying
of her feelings, she turned away to conceal. The baron 155
was subdued at once. He kissed his daughter, held out
his hand to the friar, and said, " Sing on, in God's name,
and crack away the flasks till your voice swims in
canary."

PEACOCK
(1785-1866)

an overshot mill : *a mill driven by water that " shoots over "
the top of the wheel*

flash-boards : *or flush-boards, boards placed at the side of a mill-lead
to increase the depth of water*

Ajax : *a Greek who fought against Troy. He was famed for his
strength.*

in terrorem : *to cause terror*   coit: *quoit*

canary : *a sweet wine*

1. Support each of the following opinions by one or more
   references to the passage you have just read :
   (*a*) In spite of what befell at Rubygill, Matilda has preserved
        her gaiety of spirit.
   (*b*) She does not allow her father's anger to irritate her.
   (*c*) The Baron is not so much angry, as determined to be
        angry.
   (*d*) One, at least, of his replies to his daughter is too neat to
        come from a furiously angry man.
   (*e*) Even when his wrath does boil up, it quickly cools again.

2. Why is it that the impression left by the passage as a whole
   is one of cheerfulness, not gloom ?

3. Show from lines 1-62 :
   (*a*) That Matilda may be fond of poetry ;
   (*b*) That the Baron probably prefers prose.

4. Why did Matilda's first stanza (lines 63-67) prompt the friar
   to sing " Follow, Oh Follow ! " ?

5. On earlier pages of this book contrasts have been drawn
   between poetry and prose. (See, especially, questions and
   notes on " Hawke " and " Milk for the Cat ", pages 22, 54,
   146, 163.)
   Why does it seem perfectly right that Matilda and the friar
   should abandon the prose in which this dispute begins an'
   turn to poetry (line 63) ?

Notes : 165.

From EPPING HUNT

"Epping Hunt" is a long humorous poem describing the misadventures of John Huggins, grocer, of Cheapside, who rode out one Easter Monday, a hundred years and more ago, to take part in a stag hunt over Epping Common.

His fellow-sportsmen were, most of them, Londoners like himself :

Butchers on backs of butchers' hacks,
    That shambled to and fro !
Bakers intent upon a buck,
    Neglectful of the dough !

Change Alley Bears to speculate,   5
    As usual, for a fall ;
And green and scarlet runners, such
    As never climbed a wall !

'Twas strange to think what difference
    A single creature made ;   10
A single stag had caused a whole
    Stagnation in their trade. . . .

Now Huggins from his saddle rose,
    And in the stirrups stood :
And lo ! a little cart that came   15
    Hard by a little wood ;

In shape like half a hearse—though not
    For corpses in the least,
For this contained the deer alive,
    And not the dear deceased !   20

And now began a sudden stir,
    And then a sudden shout ;
The prison-doors were opened wide,
    And Robin bounded out ! . . .

Some lost their stirrups, some their whips,
    Some had no caps to show ;
But few, like Charles at Charing Cross,
    Rode on in Statue quo.   25

" Oh dear ! Oh dear ! " now might you hear,
    " I've surely broke a bone ; "
" My head is sore," with many more   30
    Such speeches from the thrown. . . .

About two score there were, not more,
    That galloped in the race :
The rest, alas ! lay on the grass,   35
    As once in Chevy Chase !

But even those that galloped on
    Were fewer every minute :
The field kept getting more select,
    Each thicket served to thin it. . . .   40

And by their side see Huggins ride,
    As fast as he could speed ;
For, like Mazeppa, he was quite
    At mercy of his steed.

" Hold hard ! Hold hard ! you'll lame the dogs." 45
    Quoth Huggins, " So I do :
I've got the saddle well in hand,
    And hold as hard as you ! "

And rowing with his legs the while,
    As tars are apt to ride,   50
With every kick he gave a prick,
    Deep in the horse's side !

But soon the horse was well avenged
    For cruel smart of spurs,
For, riding through a moor, he pitched   55
    His master in a furze !

65

3

Where, sharper set than hunger is,
    He squatted all forlorn ;
And, like a bird, was singing out
    While sitting on a thorn !   60

Right glad was he, as well might be,
    Such cushion to resign :
" Possession is nine points," but his
    Seemed more than ninety-nine.

Yet worse than all the prickly points   65
    That entered in his skin,
His nag was running off the while
    The thorns were running in ! . . .

And let the chase again take place,
    For many a long, long year,   70
John Huggins will not ride again
    To hunt the Epping Deer !

Thus pleasure oft eludes our grasp,
    Just when we think to grip her ;
And, hunting after happiness,   75
    We only hunt a slipper.

HOOD
(1799-1845)

Change Alley Bears : *brokers who undertook to supply shares to clients at a certain date and a certain price, in the hope that the shares would fall before they must buy to fulfil their contract. Change Alley was the resort of stockbrokers before the London Stock Exchange was created.*

Robin   *the stag*

Charles at Charing Cross : *a famous equestrian statue of Charles I*

Chevy Chase : *the scene of the famous fight between Percy and Douglas,* 1388

Mazeppa : *a Polish youth punished for an offence by being bound to the back of a wild horse which was then lashed and set free. He survived, to become a great Cossack leader.*

1. What do you find amusing (*a*) in the story, (*b*) in **the** poet's way of telling it ?

2. Choose what you consider the most amusing stanza.

Notes : page 166.

From HUDIBRAS

Our brethren of New England use
Choice malefactors to excuse,
And hang the guiltless in their stead,
Of whom the churches have less need ;
As lately 't happened : In a town   5
There lived a cobbler, and but one,
That out of doctrine could cut use,
And mend men's lives, as well as shoes.
This precious brother having slain
In times of peace an Indian,   10
Not out of malice, but mere zeal,
Because he was an Infidel,
The mighty Tottipottymoy
Sent to our elders an envoy,
Complaining sorely of the breach   15
Of league held forth by Brother Patch,
For which he craved the saints to render
Into his hands, or hang, th' offender.
But they, maturely having weighed
They had no more but him o' th' trade   20
(A man that served them in a double
Capacity, to teach and cobble)
Resolved to spare him ; yet to do
The Indian Hoghan Moghan, too,
Impartial justice, in his stead did   25
Hang an old weaver that was bed-rid.

BUTLER
(1612-1680)

Our brethren of New England : *Puritan colonists in North
America.   (In the passage one Puritan is talking to another.)*
Hoghan Moghan : *potentate (from three Dutch words, meaning
" high and mighty ")*

1. Show that Butler did not like Puritans.
2. Why does the passage amuse us ?
3. What would have been lost, had Butler written in prose ?

   Notes : page 166.

MEDDLESOME MATTY

One ugly trick has often spoiled
  The sweetest and the best ;
Matilda, though a pleasant child,
  One ugly trick possessed,
Which, like a cloud before the skies,   5
Hid all her better qualities.

Sometimes she'd lift the tea-pot lid,
  To peep at what was in it ;
Or tilt the kettle, if you did
  But turn your back a minute ;   10
In vain you told her not to touch,
Her trick of meddling grew so much.

Her grandmamma went out one day,
  And by mistake she laid
Her spectacles and snuff-box gay   15
  Too near the little maid.
" Ah, well ! " thought she, " I'll try them on,
As soon as grandmamma is gone."

Forthwith she placed upon her nose
  The glasses large and wide,   20
And looking round, as I suppose,
  The snuff-box, too, she spied :
" Oh ! what a pretty box is that ;
I'll open it," said little Mat.

" I know that grandmamma would say,   25
  ' Don't meddle with it, dear ; '
But then, she's far enough away,
  And no one else is near ;
Besides, what can there be amiss
In opening such a box as this ? "   30

So thumb and finger went to work
  To move the stubborn lid ;
And presently a mighty jerk
  The mighty mischief did ;

For all at once, ah ! woeful case,   35
The snuff came puffing in her face.

Poor eyes and nose, and mouth beside,
    A dismal sight presented ;
In vain, as bitterly she cried,
    Her folly she repented.   40
In vain she ran about for ease,
She could do nothing now but sneeze.

She dashed the spectacles away
    To wipe her tingling eyes ;
And as in twenty bits they lay,   45
    Her grandmamma she spies.
" Hey-day ! and what's the matter now ? "
Says grandmamma, with lifted brow.

Matilda, smarting with the pain,
    And tingling still, and sore,
Made many a promise to refrain   50
    From meddling evermore.
And 'tis a fact, as I have heard,
She ever since has kept her word.

ANN TAYLOR
(1782-1866)

This is a pleasant and friendly example of the verse that
was once considered " most wholesome " for young readers.
    In the early days of the nineteenth century " books for the
young " were not written merely to entertain. The place of
to-day's adventure story was filled by the " moral tale " in
which " bad " boys or girls could safely be trusted to meet
fitting punishment in the turning of a page. If, for instance,
they went skating without their parents' permission, the ice
was sure to break. Verse writers, too, set store by " lessons ".
They forgot that " poesy only instructs as it delights ", and
were apt to say, like the Duchess in " Alice ", " Everything's
got a moral, if only we can find it."
    Is " Meddlesome Matty " to be called poetry or not ? Does
it delight or merely instruct ?
    Now read " Matilda " (page 70) and see how Mr. Belloc
handles the " moral tale " to-day.

Note : page 167.

MATILDA

Who told Lies, and was Burned to Death

Matilda told such Dreadful Lies,
It made one Gasp and stretch one's Eyes;
Her Aunt, who, from her Earliest Youth,
Had kept a Strict Regard for Truth,
Attempted to Believe Matilda: 5
The effort very nearly killed her,
And would have done so, had not She
Discovered this Infirmity.
For once, towards the Close of Day,
Matilda, growing tired of play,   10
And finding she was left alone,
Went tiptoe to the Telephone
And summoned the Immediate Aid
Of London's Noble Fire-Brigade.
Within an hour the Gallant Band   15
Were pouring in on every hand,
From Putney, Hackney Downs, and Bow.
With Courage high and Hearts a-glow
They galloped, roaring through the Town,
" Matilda's House is Burning Down ! "   20
Inspired by British Cheers and Loud
Proceeding from the Frenzied Crowd,
They ran their ladders through a score
Of windows on the Ball Room Floor ;
And took Peculiar Pains to Souse   25
The Pictures up and down the House,
Until Matilda's Aunt succeeded
In showing them they were not needed.
And even then she had to pay
To get the Men to go away !   30

  .   .   .   .   .   .

It happened that a few Weeks later
Her Aunt was off to the Theatre

To see that Interesting Play
The Second Mrs. Tanqueray.
She had refused to take her Niece   35
To hear this Entertaining Piece :
A Deprivation Just and Wise
To Punish her for Telling Lies.
That Night a Fire *did* break out—
You should have heard Matilda Shout !   40
You should have heard her Scream and Bawl,
And throw the window up and call
To People passing in the Street—
(The rapidly increasing Heat
Encouraging her to obtain   45
Their confidence)—but all in vain !
For every time She shouted " Fire ! "
They only answered " Little Liar ! "
And therefore when her Aunt returned,
Matilda, and the House, were Burned.   50

Hilaire Belloc (20th Century)

1. Which story do you find more easy to believe—" Meddlesome Matty " or " Matilda " ?
2. When did you first discover you were not to take " Matilda " too seriously ?
3. Compare with " Matilda ", Æsop's fable of " The Shepherd-boy who cried ' Wolf ! ' " The fable " is designed to drive home a useful moral lesson." Is " Matilda " ?
4. Rewrite in your own words lines 13, 14 of " Matilda ". Find other lines in the poem that are written in a similar style. Why does the author adopt it ?
   Why are lines 47, 48 especially funny ?
5. Why does Mr. Belloc use capital letters so freely ?
   Rewrite stanza 1 of " Meddlesome Matty ", using capitals in the " Matilda " manner.
6. Read the note on moral tales, page 69. What does Mr. Belloc seem to have found amusing in them ?
   What might we poke fun at in " Meddlesome Matty " ?
7. We have laughed at the Baron in " Follow, Oh Follow ! " at John Huggins in " Epping Hunt ", at the Puritans in the passage from " Hudibras ", and now at Matilda. Have we laughed at them all for the same reason ? See " Epping Hunt ", note 1 (*a*) (page 166), and " Hudibras ", note 2 (page 166).

Notes : page 168.

71

THE SONG OF THE CYCLOPS

We shoe the horses of the sun,
Harness the dragons of the moon,
Forge Cupid's quiver, bow, and arrows,
And his dame's coach that's drawn with sparrows ;
    Till thwick-a-thwack, thwick, thwack-a-thwack, thwack 5
    Make our brawny sinews crack ;
    Then pit-a-pat, pit, pat-a-pat, pat,
    Till thickest bars be beaten flat.

The grate which, shut, the day outbars,
Those golden studs which nail the stars,   10
The globe's case and the axle-tree,
Who can hammer these but we ?

A warming-pan to heat earth's bed,
Lying i' the frozen zone half-dead ;
Hob-nails to serve the man i' the moon,   15
And sparrowbills to clout Pan's shoon,
Whose work but ours ?
    Till thwick-a-thwack, thwick, thwack-a-thwack, thwack
    Make our brawny sinews crack ;
    Then pit-a-pat, pit, pat-a-pat, pat,   20
    Till thickest bars be beaten flat.

From London's Tempe (1629) by THOMAS DEKKER

sparrowbills : *sparables, bill-like nails used by shoemakers*
Pan : *the god of shepherds and other country-men*
Tempe : *a valley in Thessaly, famed for its beauty*
   Read the note on " London's Tempe ", page 169.

1. Are all the Cyclops' tasks worthy of gods ?
2. Why did the poet change the " thwick-a-thwack " of line
    5 to the " pit-a-pat " of line 7 ?
3. (*a*) Lines 1-4. How many beats, three or four, are there in
      each ?
   (*b*) Line 5. Write out this line and mark the beats.
4. How will you read this poem ?

Notes : page 169.

ELDORADO

Gaily bedight,
A gallant knight
  In sunshine and in shadow
Had journeyed long,
Singing a song,   5
  In search of Eldorado.

But he grew old,
This knight so bold,
  And o'er his heart a shadow
Fell, as he found   10
No spot of ground
  That looked like Eldorado.

And, as his strength
Failed him at length
  He met a pilgrim shadow.   15
" Shadow," said he,
" Where can it be,
  This land of Eldorado ? "

" Over the Mountains
Of the Moon,   20
  Down the valley of the Shadow,
Ride, boldly ride,"
The shade replied,
  " If you seek for Eldorado."

EDGAR ALLAN POE
(1809-1849)

Eldorado : *a legendary land of gold*   bedight : *arrayed*
1. Who is the pilgrim shadow (line 15) ?
2. What meanings do you give here to the Mountains of the Moon, the valley of the Shadow, Eldorado ?
3. What description have we of the knight and his journey ?
4. Would the poem be improved by the addition of a fifth stanza telling that the knight struggled on, and that with his last breath he murmured " Eldorado " ?
5. Which lines open on a " beat ", or stressed syllable ? Rewrite stanza 1, so that lines 1 and 5 open as do the others. Compare the more regular rhythm of the new stanza with the rhythm of the original.

Notes : page 170.

73

MY BONNIE MARY

Go fetch to me a pint o' wine,
  And fill it in a silver tassie,
That I may drink before I go
  A service to my bonnie lassie.
The boat rocks at the pier o' Leith,
  Fu' loud the wind blaws frae the Ferry.
The ship rides by the Berwick-law,
  And I maun leave my bonnie Mary.

The trumpets sound, the banners fly,
  The glittering spears are rankéd ready;   10
The shouts o' war are heard afar,
  The battle closes thick and bloody;
But it's no' the roar o' sea or shore
  Wad make me langer wish to tarry;
Nor shouts o' war that's heard afar—   15
  It's leaving thee, my bonnie Mary.

BURNS
(1759-1796)

tassie : *cup*   the Ferry : *Queensferry, up river from Leith*
Berwick-law : *a hill at the mouth of the Firth of Forth*
maun : *must*   service : *toast*

THE FAREWELL

It was a' for our rightfu' king
  We left fair Scotland's strand;
It was a' for our rightfu' king
  We e'er saw Irish land,
My dear,   5
  We e'er saw Irish land.

Now a' is done that men can do,
    And a' is done in vain ;
My love and native land, farewell,
    For I maun cross the main,   10
My dear,
    For I maun cross the main.

He turned him right and round about
    Upon the Irish shore ;
And gae his bridle-reins a shake,   15
    With : Adieu for evermore,
My dear,
    With : Adieu for evermore !

The sodger frae the wars returns,
    The sailor frae the main ;   20
But I hae parted frae my love,
    Never to meet again,
My dear,
    Never to meet again.

When day is gane, and night is come,   25
    And a' folk bound to sleep
I think on him that's far awa'
    The lee-lang night, and weep,
My dear,
    The lee-lang night, and weep.   30
                               BURNS
                           (1759-1796)

1. Who speaks in " My Bonnie Mary " ?
2. Who speaks (a) in lines 1-12, (b) in lines 19-30, of " The
     Farewell " ?
3. The first four lines of each stanza convey the meaning of
     " The Farewell ". What has the poet gained by the
     addition of lines 5 and 6 ?
4. In each poem a man is leaving his country and the
     woman he loves. Why do the poems affect us so
     differently ?

Notes : page 171.

JOHN O' LORN

My plaid is on my shoulder and my boat is on the shore,
  And it's all bye wi' auld days and you ;
Here's a health and here's a heartbreak, for its hame, my
      dear, no more,
  To the green glens, the fine glens we knew !

'Twas for the sake o' glory, but oh ! woe upon the wars, 5
  That brought my father's son to sic a day ;
I'd rather be a craven wi' nor fame nor name nor scars,
  Than turn an exile's heel on Moidart Bay.

And you, in the day-time, you'll be here, and in the mirk,
  Wi' the kind heart, the open hand and free ; 10
And far awa' in foreign France, in town or camp or kirk,
  I'll be wondering if you keep a thought for me.

But never more the heather nor the bracken at my knees,
  I'm poor John o' Lorn, a broken man ;
For an auld Hielan' story I must sail the swinging seas, 15
  A chief without a castle or a clan.

My plaid is on my shoulder and my boat is on the shore,
  And it's all bye wi' auld days and you ;
Here's a health and here's a heartbreak, for it's hame, my
      dear, no more,
  To the green glens, the fine glens we knew ! 20

Neil Munro
(20th Century)

Moidart Bay : *on the west coast of Inverness-shire. It was here
that Prince Charles had landed with his seven followers.*
an auld Hielan' story : *the loyalty of the chiefs to the Stewart line*
all bye : *all over*   a health : *a toast*

1. Which is the braver soldier, the speaker in " The Farewell ",
   or John o' Lorn ?
2. Read again the last paragraph in note 3 on " The Farewell ".
   Does John o' Lorn speak too much ?
3. Which stanza of the poem do you like best ?
4. What does the poem gain from the repetition of the first
   stanza ?

Notes : page 172.

CORONACH

He is gone on the mountain,
  He is lost to the forest,
Like a summer-dried fountain,
  When our need was the sorest.
The font, reappearing,   5
  From the rain-drops shall borrow,
But to us comes no cheering,
  To Duncan no morrow!

The hand of the reaper
  Takes the ears that are hoary,   10
But the voice of the weeper
  Wails manhood in glory.
The autumn winds rushing
  Waft the leaves that are searest,
But our flower was in flushing,   15
  When blighting was nearest.

Fleet foot on the correi,
  Sage counsel in cumber,
Red hand in the foray,
  How sound is thy slumber!   20
Like the dew on the mountain,
  Like the foam on the river,
Like the bubble on the fountain,
  Thou art gone, and for ever!

Scott
(1771-1832)

coronach : *funeral lament*   fountain : *spring*
correi : *a hollow in the side of a mountain*   cumber : *trouble*

1. Show that Duncan was worthy to be mourned.
2. Why do the mourners make so many references to nature?
3. See " John o' Lorn ", question 4. Would this poem be
   improved by the repetition of the first stanza after the
   third?
4. Think of those four poems, " My Bonnie Mary ", " The
   Farewell ", " John o' Lorn ", " Coronach ".
   Have you found them easy or hard to understand?
5. Can you lay down any rule as to the rhythm in which a
   sad poem should be written?

Notes : page 173.

THE FIGHTING TÉMÉRAIRE

It was eight bells ringing,
  For the morning watch was done,
And the gunner's lads were singing
  As they polished every gun.
It was eight bells ringing,   5
And the gunner's lads were singing,
For the ship she rode a-swinging
  As they polished every gun.

Oh! to see the linstock lighting,
  Téméraire! Téméraire!   10
Oh! to hear the round shot biting,
  Téméraire! Téméraire!
Oh! to see the linstock lighting,
And to hear the round shot biting,
For we're all in love with fighting   15
  On the Fighting Téméraire.

It was noontide ringing,
  And the battle just begun,
When the ship her way was winging
  As they loaded every gun.   20
It was noontide ringing,
When the ship her way was winging,
And the gunner's lads were singing
  As they loaded every gun.

There'll be many grim and gory,   25
  Téméraire! Téméraire!
There'll be few to tell the story,
  Téméraire! Téméraire!
There'll be many grim and gory,
There'll be few to tell the story,   30
But we'll all be one in glory
  With the fighting Téméraire!

There's a far bell ringing
    At the setting of the sun,
And a phantom voice is singing   35
    Of the great days done.
There's a far bell ringing,
And a phantom voice is singing
Of renown for ever clinging
    To the great days done.   40

Now the sunset breezes shiver,
    Téméraire ! Téméraire !
And she's fading down the river,
    Téméraire ! Téméraire !
Now the sunset breezes shiver,   45
And she's fading down the river,
But in England's song for ever
    She's the Fighting Téméraire.

Sir Henry Newbolt
(*20th Century*)

morning-watch : *the name given on board ship to the period of
time, 4 a.m. to 8 a.m.*

linstock : *a short, iron-shod stick which held the match used to
fire old-time cannon*

For an account of the *Téméraire* see page 174.

1. Why has the poet chosen to write of morning, noon,
    sunset ?

2. Why has he printed every other stanza in italics ?

3. (*a*) Study the rhyme-scheme of each stanza.

    (*b*) What difference do you note between the rhymes of
        stanzas 1, 3, 5 and those of stanzas 2, 4, 6 ?

    (*c*) Suggest reasons for the poet's repetition of rhymes
        and lines.

4. Why did the poet write this poem in a quieter, softer tone
    than that he adopted in " Hawke " (page 21) ?

Notes : page 174.

SPRING, THE SWEET SPRING

Spring, the sweet Spring, is the year's pleasant king;
Then blooms each thing, then maids dance in a ring,
Cold doth not sting, the pretty birds do sing,
   Cuckoo, jug-jug, pu-we, to-witta-woo.

The palm and may make country houses gay,   5
Lambs frisk and play, the shepherds pipe all day,
And we hear aye birds tune this merry lay,
   Cuckoo, jug-jug, pu-we, to-witta-woo.

The fields breathe sweet, the daisies kiss our feet,
Young lovers meet, old wives a-sunning sit,   10
In every street these tunes our ears do greet,
   Cuckoo, jug-jug, pu-we, to-witta-woo.
      Spring! the sweet Spring!

THOMAS NASH
(1567-1601)

palm : *branches of willow or hazel*

1. Which " pretty birds " sing in line 4 ?

2. Write out the rhyme-scheme of stanza 1. Do not forget
the mid-rhymes.
Are stanzas 2 and 3 written on the same scheme ?
What effect has the poet produced by rhyming so
frequently on the one sound ?

3. Why did the poet make use of so few conjunctions ?

4. Compose a stanza in Nash's manner, dealing with the sports
of the season. Retain line 4. Remember the mid-
rhymes in lines 1-3.

5. What tells us, apart from the poet's mention of them,
that the song of birds was in his ear as he wrote ?

6. Why did the poet add line 13 to the last stanza ? Will you
read it as you read the first part of line 1 ?

Notes : page 176.

THE MERRY BEGGARS

Come, come away! The spring,
By every bird that can but sing
Or chirp a note, doth now invite
Us forth to taste of his delight,
In field, in grove, on hill, in dale ;   5
But above all the nightingale.
Who in her sweetness strives to outdo
The loudness of the hoarse cuckoo.
   " Cuckoo," cries he ; " Jug, jug, jug," sings she ;
   From bush to bush, from tree to tree ;   10
   Why in one place, then, tarry we ?

Come away ! why do we stay ?
We have no debt or rent to pay ;
No bargains or accompts to make,
Nor land or lease to let or take :   15
Or if we had, should that remore us
When all the world 's our own before us,
And where we pass and make resort,
It is our kingdom and our court ?
   " Cuckoo," cries he ; " Jug, jug, jug," sings she ; 20
   From bush to bush, from tree to tree ;
   Why in one place, then, tarry we ?

RICHARD BROME
(1600 ?-1650 ?)

remore : *hinder*

1. Which of the poems you have read in earlier pages express
   a similar delight in the open air ?

2. Which line sounds most cheerful, most full of the joy of
   Spring ?

3. Which poet, Nash or Brome, is more enraptured by the
   sheer joy of the season ?

Notes : page 176.

A SPRING SCENE

Thursday, 15th April . . . It rained and blew, when we went to bed.

Friday, 16th April (Good Friday)—When I undrew my curtains in the morning, I was much affected by the beauty of the prospect, and the change. The sun shone, the wind had passed away, the hills looked cheerful, the river was very bright as it flowed into the lake. . . . When we came to the foot of Brothers Water, I left William sitting on the bridge and went along the path on the right side of the lake through the wood. I was delighted with what I saw. The water under the boughs of the bare old trees, the simplicity of the mountains and the exquisite beauty of the path. . . . When I returned, I found William writing a poem descriptive of the sights and sounds we saw and heard. There was the gentle flowing of the stream, the glittering, lively lake, green fields without a living creature to be seen on them ; behind us, a flat pasture with forty-two cattle feeding ; to our left, the road leading to the hamlet. No smoke there, the sun shone on the bare roofs. The people were at work, ploughing, harrowing, and sowing ; . . . a dog barking now and then, cocks crowing, birds twittering, the snow in patches at the top of the highest hills, yellow palms, purple and green twigs on the birches, ashes with their glittering spikes quite bare. The hawthorn a bright green, with black stems under the oak. The moss of the oak glossy. . . .

Dorothy Wordsworth
(1771-1855)

Brothers Water : *a little lake, some two miles south of Ullswater*
palms : *catkins*

This passage comes from the Diary, or Journal, of the poet's sister and devoted companion. She was like her brother in many ways. Her eyes were as quick as his to see the beautiful things of the world, and her hand as ready to set down what she saw.

Because she was a prose writer, and her brother a poet, you may find it interesting to compare this page with the one which follows.

LINES WRITTEN IN MARCH

(*While resting on the bridge at the foot of Brothers Water*)

<pre>
    The cock is crowing,
    The stream is flowing,
    The small birds twitter,
    The lake doth glitter,
The green field sleeps in the sun ;   5
    The oldest and youngest
    Are at work with the strongest ;
    The cattle are grazing,
    Their heads never raising ;
There are forty feeding like one !   10

    Like an army defeated
    The snow hath retreated,
    And now doth fare ill
    On the top of the bare hill ;
The plough-boy is whooping—anon—anon :   15
    There's joy in the mountains ;
    There's life in the fountains ;
    Small clouds are sailing,
    Blue sky prevailing ;
The rain is over and gone !   20
</pre>

WILLIAM WORDSWORTH
(1770-1850)

The poem was written in 1802, but not published till 1807.   By that time it would seem that Wordsworth had forgotten the month of its composition.

1. Which details of the scene are given only in the prose ?
2. Which details are given only in the poem ?
3. Why did the poet make no reference to the trees ?
4. Read again " November Days " (page 45).   What has Wordsworth's scene in common with Clare's ?
5. Which line in this poem will you read most quietly ?
6. Has the poem a good beginning and a good ending ?
7. Dorothy Wordsworth tells us she was delighted with what she saw (line 10).   What tells us that the poet was delighted ?

Notes : page 177.

HOME THOUGHTS FROM ABROAD

Oh, to be in England,
Now that April's there,
And whoever wakes in England
Sees, some morning, unaware,
That the lowest boughs and the brushwood sheaf   5
Round the elm-tree bole are in tiny leaf,
While the chaffinch sings on the orchard bough
In England—now !

And after April, when May follows,
And the whitethroat builds, and all the swallows !   10
Hark, where my blossomed pear-tree in the hedge
Leans to the field and scatters on the clover
Blossoms and dewdrops—at the bent spray's edge—
That's the wise thrush ; he sings each song twice over,
Lest you should think he never could recapture   15
The first fine careless rapture !

And though the fields look rough with hoary dew,
All will be gay when noontide wakes anew
The buttercups, the little children's dower
—Far brighter than this gaudy melon-flower.   20

BROWNING
(1812-1889)

unaware : *without expecting it*
brushwood sheaf : *cluster of small twigs at the foot of the*
trunk   whitethroat : *a summer visitant to England*

1. Where was the poet when he wrote this poem ?
2. (*a*) How many pictures of the English Spring are here ?
   (*b*) At what time of the day does the poet see each ?
3. (*a*) Which picture do you see most clearly ?
   (*b*) Why " the wise thrush " ?
4. What in the English Spring does the poet seem to long
      for most ?
5. Is this a sad or a happy poem ?
6. (*a*) Which poem on an earlier page is written, like this,
      to no set stanza-pattern ?
   (*b*) Is the irregular form of " Home Thoughts " a beauty
      or a blemish ?

Notes : page 178.

DIVINATION BY A DAFFODIL

When a daffodil I see,
Hanging down his head towards me,
Guess I may, what I must be :
First, I shall decline my head ;
Secondly, I shall be dead ;   5
Lastly, safely buried.

HERRICK
(1591-1674)

OF BEAUTY

Let us use it while we may
Snatch those joys that haste away.
Earth her winter coat may cast,
And renew her beauty past ;
But, our winter come, in vain   5
We solicit Spring again ;
And when our furrows snow shall cover,
Love may return, but never lover.

SIR RICHARD FANSHAWE
(1608-1666)

divination : *foretelling of the future*

1. Do the poems on this page contradict those on pages
   80-84 ?

2. Would you call these poems sad or serious ?
   Compare them with " The Farewell " (page 75) and
   " Coronach " (page 77).

Notes : page 178.

JOCK O' HAZLEDEAN

" Why weep ye by the tide, ladie ?
   Why weep ye by the tide ?
I'll wed ye to my youngest son,
   And ye sall be his bride :
And ye sall be his bride, ladie,
   Sae comely to be seen "—
But aye she loot the tears down fa'
   For Jock o' Hazledean.

" Now let this wilfu' grief be done,
   And dry that cheek so pale ;
Young Frank is chief of Errington,
   And lord of Langley-dale ;
His step is first in peaceful ha',
   His sword in battle keen "—
But aye she loot the tears down fa'
   For Jock o' Hazledean.

" A chain of gold ye sall not lack,
   Nor braid to bind your hair—
Nor mettled hound, nor managed hawk,
   Nor palfrey fresh and fair ;
And you, the foremost o' them a',
   Shall ride our forest queen "—
But aye she loot the tears down fa'
   For Jock o' Hazledean.

The kirk was deck'd at morning-tide,
   The tapers glimmer'd fair ;
The priest and bridegroom wait the bride.
   And dame and knight are there.
They sought her baith by bower and ha' :
   The ladie was not seen !
She's o'er the Border, and awa'
   Wi' Jock o' Hazledean.

SCOTT
(1771-1832)

loot : *let*   bower : *ladies' apartments in a great house*
managed : *trained*

1. Which line tells you whether the lady is English or Scots ?

2. Who speaks in stanza 1 ?

3. Who speaks in stanza 2 ?

4. (*a*) Who speaks in stanza 3 ?
   (*b*) In which poem earlier in this book have you read of similar bribes offered to a lady ?

5. (*a*) The first stanza is old, the others are Scott's. What resemblances do you find between this poem and the ballads you have read ? See particularly " Get up and Bar the Door " (page 36) " Annan Water " (page 38) and the notes to the latter (page 153).
   (*b*) Has Scott kept as closely to the ballad style as does his original ?

6. Has Scott imitated the original form in every detail ?

Notes : page 179.

LOCHINVAR

Oh, young Lochinvar is come out of the west,
Through all the wide Border his steed was the best,
And save his good broadsword he weapons had none,
He rode all unarmed, and he rode all alone.
So faithful in love, and so dauntless in war,   5
There never was knight like the young Lochinvar.

He stayed not for brake, and he stopped not for stone,
He swam the Eske river where ford there was none ;
But ere he alighted at Netherby gate
The bride had consented, the gallant came late ;   10
For a laggard in love and a dastard in war
Was to wed the fair Ellen of brave Lochinvar.

So boldly he entered the Netherby Hall,
Among bride's-men, and kinsmen, and brothers, and all ;
Then spoke the bride's father, his hand on his sword   15
(For the poor craven bridegroom said never a word)
" Oh come ye in peace here, or come ye in war,
Or to dance at our bridal, young Lord Lochinvar ? "

" I long woo'd your daughter, my suit you denied ;
Love swells like the Solway, but ebbs like its tide ;   20
And now I am come, with this lost love of mine.
To lead but one measure, drink one cup of wine.
There are maidens in Scotland more lovely by far,
That would gladly be bride to the young Lochinvar."

The bride kiss'd the goblet ; the knight took it up,   25
He quaff'd off the wine, and he threw down the cup.
She look'd down to blush, and she look'd up to sigh,
With a smile on her lips and a tear in her eye.
He took her soft hand ere her mother could bar,
" Now tread we a measure ! " said young Lochinvar.   30

So stately his form, and so lovely her face,
That never a hall such a galliard did grace ;
While her mother did fret, and her father did fume,
And the bridegroom stood dangling his bonnet and plume ;
And the bridemaidens whispered, " 'Twere better by far   35
To have matched our fair cousin with young Lochinvar."

One touch to her hand, and one word in her ear,
When they reached the hall door, and the charger stood near,
So light to the croupe the fair lady he swung,
So light to the saddle before her he sprung,   40
" She is won ! we are gone ! over bank, bush, and scaur,
They'll have fleet steeds that follow," quoth young
    Lochinvar.

There was mounting 'mong Graemes of the Netherby clan ;
Forsters, Fenwicks, and Musgraves, they rode and they
    ran ;

There was racing and chasing on Cannobie Lee, 45
But the lost bride of Netherby ne'er did they see.
So daring in love and so dauntless in war,
Have ye e'er heard of gallant like young Lochinvar ?

Scott (1771-1832)

Lochinvar : *a Kirkcudbrightshire place name*
Eske river : *at one part of its course the boundary between
Scotland and England*
Netherby : *in Cumberland*   Cannobie Lee : *on the Scots Border*
galliard : *cheerful dance*   croupe : *horse's back, behind the saddle*

1. Compare the theme of this poem with that of " Jock o'
   Hazledean ".

2. Compare the attitudes of the father, the mother, the bridegroom.

3. Compare stanzas 1-4 with this version of them in plain
   prose :

   *Fair Ellen Graeme of Netherby Hall and the young Lord
   of Lochinvar had long been lovers, but her father refused his
   consent to the marriage. Then, one day, news came to Lochinvar
   that another suitor had appeared, a dull fellow and a coward,
   but rich in lands and gold. He had the strong support of the
   family, and Ellen was being hard driven to consent to an
   early marriage. Lochinvar acted at once. Mounting his steed,
   the best in all the Border country, he rode at full speed for
   Netherby. But it seemed he had come too late. Ellen's consent
   had been forced, and within an hour she was to be married. It
   was her father, not the cowardly bridegroom, who took up the
   challenge of his arrival. " Are you here as an enemy," he asked,
   " or a friend, to dance at our bridal ? " " To dance," said
   Lochinvar, " to drink one cup of wine, and to dance but one
   dance with my lost love."*

   What have you lost in the prose ?

4. Which line in this poem rings with the same triumph
   as the last two lines of " Jock o' Hazledean " ?

5. You may find it interesting to rewrite the tale in ballad
   form. Here is a possible opening stanza in the usual four-
   beat and three-beat metre :

   > *" Gae saddle me my gallant steed,*
   > *Gae saddle him, and mak' him ready ;*
   > *For mony 's the mile we'll gang this day*
   > *If we would win a bonnie lady."*

6. What effect is produced by the metre in which " Lochinvar " is
   written ?

Notes : page 180.

89

THE FIFTEEN ACRES

I cling and swing
On a branch, or sing
Through the cool, clear hush of Morning, O :
Or fling my wing
On the air, and bring   5
To sleepier birds a warning, O :
That the night's in flight,
And the sun's in sight,
And the dew is the grass adorning, O :
And the green leaves swing   10
As I sing, sing, sing,
Up by the river,
Down the dell,
To the little wee nest,
Where the big tree fell,   15
So early in the morning, O.

I flit and twit
In the sun for a bit
When his light so bright is shining, O :
Or sit and fit   20
My plumes, or knit
Straw plaits for the nest's nice lining, O :
And she with glee
Shows unto me
Underneath her wings reclining, O :   25
And I sing that Peg
Has an egg, egg, egg,
Up by the oatfield,
Round the mill,
Past the meadow,   30
Down the hill
So early in the morning, O.

I stoop and swoop
On the air, or loop
Through the trees, and then go soaring, O :   35
To group with a troop
On the gusty poop
While the wind behind is roaring, O :
I skim and swim
By a cloud's red rim   40
And up to the azure flooring, O :
And my wide wings drip
As I slip, slip, slip
Down through the rain-drops,
Back where Peg   45
Broods in the nest
On the little white egg,
So early in the morning, O.

JAMES STEPHENS
(20th Century)

1. Suggest an explanation of the title of the poem.

2. What are the gusty poop (line 37) and the azure flooring (line 41) ?

3. How many sentences are there in the poem ?

4. How many rhyming words are there in lines 1-9 of each stanza ?

5. Write down the words in each stanza that rhyme on an " i " sound, as cling, swing ; flit, twit.

6. There are 85 words in stanza 1. How many of these are words of more than one syllable ?

7. Consider your answers to questions 3, 4, 5, and 6, and say what the poet has planned to do.

8. Why did the poet change from the " i " rhymes of cling, swing, etc., to the " oo " rhymes of stoop, swoop, etc., stanza 3 ?

9. Where is the bird at the close of each stanza ?

10. How will you read this poem ?

   Notes : page 180.

MAGDALEN

Magdalen at Michael's gate
  Tirled at the pin ;
On Joseph's thorn sang the blackbird,
  " Let her in ! Let her in ! "

" Hast thou seen the wounds ? " said Michael,   5
  " Knowest thou thy sin ? "
" It is evening, evening," sang the blackbird,
  " Let her in ! Let her in ! "

" Yes, I have seen the wounds,
  And I know my sin."   10
" She knows it well, well, well," sang the blackbird,
  " Let her in ! Let her in ! "

" Thou bringest no offerings," said Michael,
  " Nought save sin."
And the blackbird sang, " She is sorry, sorry, sorry, 15
  Let her in ! Let her in ! "

When he had sung himself to sleep,
  And night did begin,
One came and opened Michael's gate,
  And Magdalen went in.   20

HENRY KINGSLEY
(1830-1876)

tirled at the pin : *rattled at the latch*

Mary Magdalen is commonly supposed to be the " woman in the city, which was a sinner " of whom Jesus said " Her sins, which are many, are forgiven; for she loved much ". (Luke, vii, 37-47).

Michael, the chief of angels, appears in the Bible as a warrior. In the poem he guards the gate of Heaven.

Legend tells that Joseph of Arimathæa came to England, and that his staff, planted by him at Glastonbury, grew into a thorn tree.

Note how beautifully Kingsley has turned the bird's evening song into words of supplication for the penitent at the gate.

1. Why has the poet not driven home the lesson of the poem in another stanza ?

Notes : page 181.

TO DAFFODILS

Fair Daffodils, we weep to see
   You haste away so soon;
As yet the early-rising sun
   Has not attain'd his noon.
       Stay, stay,   5
     Until the hasting day
       Has run
   But to the even-song ;
And, having prayed together, we
   Will go with you along.   10

We have short time to stay, as you ;
   We have as short a spring ;
As quick a growth to meet decay,
   As you, or anything.
       We die   15
   As your hours do, and dry
       Away,
   Like to the summer's rain ;
Or as the pearls of morning dew,
   Ne'er to be found again.   20

HERRICK
(1591-1674)

even-song : *the time of evening prayer*

1. Read again " Divination by a Daffodil " (page 85).
   Which line in it may explain why this flower should have suggested so strongly to Herrick the idea of the " hasting day " ?

2. (*a*) Write out the rhyme-scheme for stanza 1. Is it repeated in stanza 2 ?

   (*b*) What would we have lost had the poet written lines 5-8 in two lines, instead of four ?

3. Lines 15-20.
   (*a*) To which lines in " Coronach " (page 77) may those be compared ?

   (*b*) Which passage, Scott's or Herrick's, do you prefer ?

Notes : page 182.

DAFFODILS

I wandered lonely as a cloud
   That floats on high o'er vales and hills,
When all at once I saw a crowd,
   A host of golden daffodils ;
Beside the lake, beneath the trees,   5
Fluttering and dancing in the breeze.

Continuous as the stars that shine
   And twinkle on the Milky Way,
They stretched in never-ending line
   Along the margin of a bay :   10
Ten thousand saw I at a glance,
Tossing their heads in sprightly dance.

The waves beside them danced, but they
   Outdid the sparkling waves in glee :
A poet could not but be gay,   15
   In such a jocund company :
I gazed—and gazed—but little thought
What wealth the show to me had brought :

For oft, when on my couch I lie
   In vacant or in pensive mood,   20
They flash upon that inward eye
   Which is the bliss of solitude ;
And then my heart with pleasure fills
And dances with the daffodils.

WILLIAM WORDSWORTH (1770-1850)

the Milky Way : *a band of light in the heavens formed of myriads of stars which the naked eye cannot distinguish, one from another*

1. Picture the scene the poet saw. Was the wind blowing ? Was the sun shining ?
2. Why did he compare the daffodils to the stars ?
3. Line 16. Why a *jocund company* ?
4. Contrast the descriptions the poet gives of himself in stanza 1 and in stanza 3.
5. (*a*) Which two words in stanza 4 describe the daffodils ?
   (*b*) How often have you been told, not necessarily in these words, that the daffodils flashed and danced ?
6. Line 18. What wealth had the show brought to the poet ?

Notes : page 182.

A BUSY HIGHWAY

Thursday, 15th April, 1802 . . . When we were in
the woods beyond Gowbarrow Park we saw a few daffodils
close to the water-side. We fancied that the lake had
floated the seeds ashore, and that the little colony had
so sprung up. But as we went along there were more and 5
yet more ; and at last, under the boughs of the trees, we
saw that there was a long belt of them along the shore, about
the breadth of a country turnpike road. I never saw
daffodils so beautiful. They grew among the mossy
stones about and about them ; some rested their heads 10
upon these stones, as on a pillow, for weariness ; and the
rest tossed and reeled and danced, and seemed as if they
verily laughed with the wind, that blew upon them over
the lake ; they looked so gay, ever glancing, ever changing.
The wind blew directly over the lake to them. There was 15
here and there a little knot, and a few stragglers higher up ;
but they were so few as not to disturb the simplicity,
unity, and life of that one busy highway. We rested again
and again. The bays were stormy, and we heard the
waves at different distances, and in the middle of the 20
water, like the sea.

DOROTHY WORDSWORTH (1771-1855)

turnpike road : *better-class road, on which, in former times,
tolls were charged at turnpikes (spiked toll-gates)*

1. Does the prose put before you the same picture as the
   poem did ?
2. Dorothy Wordsworth tells us that first they saw a few
   daffodils, then more and more, and at last a long belt of
   them. Does this contradict the poet's " All at once" ?
3. Could the poet have made use of the " turnpike road "
   comparison (line 8) ?
4. Why did he not tell us that " some rested their heads . . .
   as on a pillow, for weariness " ?
5. Which lines of the prose most nearly capture the spirit of
   the poem ?
6. What, apart from differences of form, are the chief
   distinctions between the poetry and the prose ?

Notes : page 183.

95

GIPSY SONG

The faery beam upon you,
The stars to glister on you ;
    A moon of light
    In the noon of night,
Till the fire-drake hath o'ergone you !   5

The wheel of fortune guide you,
The boy with the bow beside you
    Run aye in the way
    Till the bird of day,
And the luckier lot betide you.

BEN JONSON
(1572-1637)

fire-drake : *fiery serpent*   o'ergone : *passed by*
the boy with the bow : *Cupid*

THE BELL-MAN

From noise of scare-fires rest ye free,
From Murders—Benedicite.
From all mischances, that may fright
Your pleasing slumbers in the night :
Mercy secure ye all, and keep   5
The Goblin from ye, while ye sleep.

    Past one o'clock, and almost two,
My masters all, Good Day to you !

HERRICK
(1591-1674)

bell-man : *the watchman who kept guard in the streets at night
and called the hours*

scare-fires : *alarms of fire*   Benedicite : *bless ye !*

These are poems of good wishes, the first for a safe journey,
the second for pleasing slumbers.

1. Would the first incite you to travel ?
2. Would the second soothe you to sleep ?

    Notes : page 184.

NIGHT PIECE TO JULIA

Her eyes the glow-worm lend thee,
The shooting stars attend thee ;
    And the elves also,
    Whose little eyes glow
Like the sparks of fire, befriend thee   5

No Will o' th' Wisp mislight thee ;
Nor snake or slow-worm bite thee ;
    But on, on thy way,
    Not making a stay,
Since ghost there is none to affright thee.   10

Let not the dark thee cumber ;
What though the moon does slumber ?
    The stars of the night
    Will lend thee their light,
Like tapers clear without number.   15

HERRICK
(1591-1674)

Will o' th' Wisp : *a light that rises from marshy ground*

slow-worm : *" slay-worm", a lizard, really, but thought to be dangerous, from its resemblance to a snake. It is often called the blind-worm.*

cumber : *hinder*

1. Did Herrick know Jonson's " Gipsy Song " (page 96) ?
2. Do the poets present the same picture of night ?
3. In which night would Julia prefer to walk ?
4. Will you read each poem at the same pace
5. Which poem do you prefer ?

Notes : page 185.

PUCK

Scene : A moonlit wood

Enter from opposite sides A FAIRY *and* PUCK.

FAIRY : Either I mistake your shape and making quite,
Or else you are that shrewd and knavish sprite
Called Robin Good-fellow. Are you not he
That frights the maidens of the villagery ;
Skim milk, and sometimes labour in the quern,   5
And bootless make the breathless housewife churn ,
And sometimes make the drink to bear no barm ;
Mislead night-wanderers, laughing at their harm ?
Those that Hobgoblin call you, and sweet Puck,
You do their work, and they shall have good luck :   10
Are not you he ?

PUCK :   Fairy, thou speak'st aright ;
I am that merry wanderer of the night.
I jest to Oberon, and make him smile,
When I a fat and bean-fed horse beguile,
Neighing in likeness of a filly foal ;   15
And sometime lurk I in a gossip's bowl,
In very likeness of a roasted crab,
And when she drinks, against her lips I bob,
And on her withered dewlap pour the ale.
The wisest aunt, telling the saddest tale,   20
Sometime for three-foot stool mistaketh me,
Then slip I from her, and down topples she,
And " tailor " cries, and falls into a cough,
And then the whole quire hold their hips and laugh,
And waxen in their mirth, and neeze and swear   25
A merrier hour was never wasted there.

From *A Midsummer Night's Dream* (*Act II, Scene I*)

SHAKESPEARE
(1564-1616)

shrewd : *mischievous*   gossip : *old woman*
quern : *grain-grinding mill, worked by hand*   crab : *crab-apple*
bootless : *to no purpose*   dewlap : *loose flesh on the throat*
barm : *froth, " head "*   neeze : *sneeze*
Oberon : *King of the fairies*

Puck is the Goblin of " The Bell-man ". He was bigger than the fairies, a " lob of spirits ", cousin to the Brownie and the Irish Leprechaun. This page and those which follow give you a full description of his ways. If you like him, you will enjoy Kipling's " Puck of Pook's Hill " and its companion book, " Rewards and Fairies ". (See page 105, and note 2, page 187.)

People of old times believed that the fairies and goblins were especially busy and powerful on Midsummer Night. (See " Lord Arnaldos ", page 123.)

1. The Fairy calls Puck a shrewd and knavish sprite, and he makes frank confession of his misdeeds. From the evidence given in the dialogue what can you find to say in his favour ?

2. Do the Fairy and Puck meet often ?

3. How will you read (*a*) the Fairy's speech ; (*b*) Puck's ?

Notes : page 185.

THE MAD AND MERRY PRANKS OF ROBIN GOOD-FELLOW

From Oberon in Fairy Land,
    The King of ghosts and shadows there,
Mad Robin I, at his command
    Am sent to view the night-sports here.
      What revel rout   5
      Is kept about,
In every corner where I go,
      I will o'ersee
      And merry be,
And make good sport, with " Ho ! Ho ! Ho ! "   10

More swift than lightning can I fly,
  And round this airy welkin soon ;
And in a minute's space, descry
  Each thing that's done below the moon.
    There's not a hag   15
    Or ghost shall wag,
Cry, ware Goblins, where I go ;
    But Robin, I,
    Their feats will spy,
And fear them home with " Ho ! Ho ! Ho ! "   20

If any wanderers I meet,
  That from their night-sports do trudge home,
With counterfeiting voice I greet,
  And call them on with me to roam.
    Through woods, through lakes,   25
    Through bogs, through brakes,
O'er bush and briar with them I go.
    I call upon
    Them to come on,
And wend me, laughing " Ho ! Ho ! Ho ! "   30

Sometimes I meet them like a man ;
  Sometimes, an ox ; sometimes, a hound ;
And to a horse I turn me can,
  To trip and trot about them round ;
    But if, to ride,   35
    My back they stride,
More swift than wind away I go.
    O'er hedge and lands,
    Through pools and ponds,
I whirry, laughing " Ho ! Ho ! Ho ! "   40

When lads and lasses merry be
  With possets and with junkets fine,
Unseen of all the company,
  I eat their cates and sip their wine.
    And to make sport   45
    I start and snort,

And out the candles I do blow.
    The maids I kiss ;
    They shriek, " Who's this ? "
I answer nought but " Ho ! Ho ! Ho ! "   50

Yet, now and then, the maids to please,
  I card, at midnight, up their wool ;
And while they sleep and take their ease,
  With wheel, to threads their flax I pull.
    I grind at mill   55
    Their malt up, still ;
I dress their hemp ; I spin their tow.
    If any wake
    And would me take,
I wend me, laughing " Ho ! Ho ! Ho ! "   60

From hag-bred Merlin's time have I
  Thus nightly revelled to and fro ;
And for my pranks men call me by
  The name of Robin Good-fellow.
    Fiends, ghosts, and sprites,   65
    That haunt the nights,
The hags and goblins, do me know.
    And beldams old
    My feats have told.
So *Valé! Valé!* Ho ! Ho ! Ho !   70

ANONYMOUS
(17th Century)

whirry : *whirl away*   possets : *drinks of hot milk and wine*
junkets : *sweetmeats*   beldams : *old hags*   Valé : *Goodbye*
hag-bred Merlin : *wizard of King Arthur's time*

1. Which of those mad and merry pranks have you heard
   of already ?
2. Does the mad Robin of this poem differ in any way from
   the merry wanderer of the last ?
3. Show that the stanza might have been written as one of
   eight lines, not ten.
   Why has the poet preferred the longer form ?

Notes : page 186.

101

FAIRY LULLABY

Scene **:** *A moonlit wood*

Enter with her train, TITANIA, *queen of the Fairies.*

TITANIA **:** Come, now a roundel and a fairy song ;
Then, for the third part of a minute, hence ;
Some to kill cankers in the musk-rose buds,
Some war with rere-mice for their leathern wings,
To make my small elves coats, and some keep back   5
The clamorous owl that nightly hoots and wonders
At our quaint spirits. Sing me now asleep ;
Then to your offices and let me rest.

Song

You spotted snakes with double tongue,
   Thorny hedgehogs, be not seen ;   10
Newts and blind-worms, do no wrong ;
   Come not near our fairy queen.

     Philomel, with melody,
     Sing in our sweet lullaby ;
Lulla, lulla, lullaby ; lulla, lulla, lullaby :   15
     Never harm,
     Nor spell nor charm,
   Come our lovely lady nigh :
   So, good night, with lullaby.

Weaving spiders, come not here ;   20
   Hence, you long-legged spinners, hence !
Beetles black, approach not near ;
   Worm nor snail, do no offence.

Philomel, with melody,
  Sing in our sweet lullaby ;   25
Lulla, lulla, lullaby ; lulla, lulla, lullaby :
    Never harm,
    Nor spell nor charm ,
  Come our lovely lady nigh :
  So, good night, with lullaby.   30

FAIRY : Hence, away ! now all is well.
         One, aloof, stand sentinel.

(Exeunt Fairies.   Titania sleeps.)

From *A Midsummer Night's Dream* (*Act II, Scene II*)

SHAKESPEARE
(1564-1616)

roundel : *dance in a ring*   quaint : *dainty, delicate, fine*
offices : *duties*   Philomel : *nightingale*
cankers : *worms that destroy the flowers*
rere-mice : *bats*

1. The fairies are sometimes called the wee folk. Could
   we use the words to describe Titania's train ?

2. Do you realise more clearly now the difference between the
   Fairies and Puck (page 98) ?

3. Is this a sleepy song ?

   Notes : page 186.

ARIEL'S SONG

Ariel, "an airy spirit", compelled for a time to serve Prospero, a great magician, has been given the promise that he will ere long be free.   He sings :

Where the bee sucks, there suck I ;
In a cowslip's bell I lie ;
There I couch when owls do cry.
On the bat's back I do fly
After summer merrily.   5
Merrily, merrily shall I live now,
Under the blossom that hangs on the bough.

From *The Tempest* (*Act V, Scene I*)

SHAKESPEARE
(1564-1616)

1. Might Ariel join Titania's train ?
   Note : page 187.

FAREWELL, REWARDS AND FAIRIES

" Farewell, rewards and fairies ! "
  Good housewives now may say ;
For now foul sluts in dairies
  Do fare as well as they.
And though they sweep their hearths no less   5
  Than maids were wont to do,
Yet who of late, for cleanliness,
  Finds sixpence in her shoe !

At morning and at evening both
  You merry were and glad ;   10
So little care of sleep or sloth
  Those pretty ladies had.
When Tom came home from labour,
  Or Ciss to milking rose,
Then merrily, merrily went their tabour.   15
  And nimbly went their toes.

Witness, those rings and roundelays
  Of theirs, which yet remain,
Were footed in Queen Mary's days,
  On many a grassy plain.   20
But since, of late, Elizabeth,
  And, later, James came in,
They never danced on any heath,
  As when the time hath been.

BISHOP RICHARD CORBET
(1582-1635)

tabour : *small drum, used to accompany dancing*
roundelays : *fairy rings ; darker circles in grass, thought at one time to be caused by fairies' dancing feet*

1. Who are (a) those pretty ladies (line 12) ; (b) Tom and
    Ciss (lines 13, 14) ; (c) Queen Mary (line 19) ?
2. Why have the fairies gone ?
3. Were those fairies more akin to Puck or to Titania ?
4. Find a line in which the poet has purposely departed from
    his metrical scheme.
5. Bishop Corbet was a favourite of James I. He hated the
    Puritans. Did he believe in fairies ?

Notes : page 187.

THE DANCING STAR

Once there was an old dancing-master,
  Once upon a time,
He was a dancing disaster,
Was this old dancing-master,
  Once upon a time.   5
Once in the life of this old fiddle scraper—
  For he fiddled as he danced,
Cutting many an ungainly caper—
  He was entranced
By the dancing of a couple   10
  Who were really stars,
Venus the lady, luminous and supple,
  And the man was Mars.
They did not look as if, but were it,
  Those dancers divine,   15
Just as Their Graces are without the coronet,
  When they go forth to dine.
So they danced, and the old fellow's fiddle
  Sang as it never sang before,
But why this happened was to him a riddle,   20
  And also why both feet kept off the floor.
" We have eloped to earth," laughed Venus as she told him
  Earth was heaven's Gretna Green,
" And, if you doubt, look skyward and behold him."
  He looked, but Mars was nowhere to be seen.   25
Only a comely warrior stood beside him ;
  Then the old man's eyes came full of stars.
" Shall we take him back with us and hide him
  Somewhere between ' Venus ' and ' Mars ' ?
He will carry word of love between us,   30
  We need a dancing star, we do indeed.
His long grey locks will stream with gold," said Venus,
  " When Mercury has given the touch of speed."
She laid one finger where his heart was beating,
  One finger divine :   35

Anguish of radiant bliss beyond repeating,
    Then he began to shine.
Soon they were far from earth and high in heaven,
    Those Lovers serene,
And on a Tuesday or a Friday even
    You may see the star that dances in between.

Once there was an old dancing-master,
    Once upon a time,
Yes, once there was an old dancing-master,
    Once upon a time,
He was a dancing disaster,
Was this old dancing-master,
    But now he is sublime.

DOUGLAS AINSLIE
(20th Century)

Venus : *Roman goddess of love*   Mars : *Roman god of war*
Mercury : *fleet-footed messenger of the gods   Three planets
    bear their names*
Their Graces : *people of high rank ; Duke and Duchess*
Gretna Green : *a village in the south of Scotland where
"eloping" couples are married*
sublime : *raised above the ordinary level ; here, raised to heaven*

When Mr. Ainslie was ten, he lived in Aberdeenshire, in a
castle two miles from Turriff. An old dancing-master used to
walk up to give a lesson, twice a week. He danced, fiddled,
and taught, all at the same time. Many, many years afterwards the author wondered what had become of him, and
the poem is the answer.

1. Are Venus and Mars gods, or planets, in the poem ?
2. Why did Venus take the dancing-master back to heaven ?
3. Line 40. Why a Tuesday or a Friday evening ?
4. What is the derivation of " disaster " ? Why is the word
    particularly apt in lines 3 and 46 ?
5. Was the poet fond of the dancing-master ?
6. Lines 42-48 :
   (*a*) Why does the poet recall lines 1-5 ?
   (*b*) What are the effects of the changes he has made ?
7. " The Dancing Star " first appeared in " The Fortnightly
    Review " some years ago. Mr. W. L. Courtney, the
    editor, said he printed it because he " never saw anything
    like it ".   What makes it " different " ?

Notes : page 188.

107

THE LADY OF SHALOTT

PART I

On either side the river lie
Long fields of barley and of rye,
That clothe the wold and meet the sky;
And thro' the field the road runs by
    To many-tower'd Camelot;
And up and down the people go,
Gazing where the lilies blow
Round an island there below,
    The island of Shalott.

Willows whiten, aspens quiver,
Little breezes dusk and shiver
Thro' the wave that runs for ever
By the island in the river
    Flowing down to Camelot.
Four grey walls, and four grey towers,
Overlook a space of flowers,
And the silent isle imbowers
    The Lady of Shalott.

By the margin, willow-veil'd,
Slide the heavy barges trail'd
By slow horses; and unhail'd
The shallop flitteth silken-sail'd
    Skimming down to Camelot:
But who hath seen her wave her hand?
Or at the casement seen her stand?
Or is she known in all the land,
    The Lady of Shalott?

wold : *open rising ground*

Only reapers, reaping early
In among the bearded barley,
Hear a song that echoes cheerly
From the river winding clearly,
    Down to tower'd Camelot :
And by the moon the reaper weary,
Piling sheaves in uplands airy,
Listening, whispers, " 'Tis the fairy
    Lady of Shalott."

PART II

There she weaves by night and day
A magic web with colours gay.
She has heard a whisper say,
A curse is on her if she stay
    To look down to Camelot.
She knows not what the curse may be,
And so she weaveth steadily,
And little other care hath she,
    The Lady of Shalott.

And moving thro' a mirror clear
That hangs before her all the year,
Shadows of the world appear.
There she sees the highway near
    Winding down to Camelot :
There the river eddy whirls,
And there the surly village-churls,
And the red cloaks of market girls,
    Pass onward from Shalott.

Sometimes a troop of damsels glad,   55
An abbot on an ambling pad,
Sometimes a curly shepherd-lad,
Or long-hair'd page in crimson clad,
    Goes by to tower'd Camelot ;
And sometimes thro' the mirror blue   60
The knights come riding two and two :
She hath no loyal knight and true,
    The Lady of Shalott.

But in her web she still delights
To weave the mirror's magic sights,   65
For often thro' the silent nights
A funeral, with plumes and lights
    And music, went to Camelot ;
Or when the moon was overhead,
Came two young lovers lately wed ;   70
" I am half sick of shadows," said
    The Lady of Shalott.

PART III

A bow-shot from her bower-eaves,
He rode between the barley-sheaves,
The sun came dazzling thro' the leaves,   75
And flamed upon the brazen greaves
    Of bold Sir Lancelot.
A red-cross knight for ever kneel'd
To a lady in his shield,
That sparkled on the yellow field,   80
    Beside remote Shalott.

an ambling pad : *a pony whose pace gives its rider a comfortable seat*

bow-shot : *three hundred yards, or so.   See page 62, line* 124.

greaves : *armour for the legs*

The gemmy bridle glitter'd free,
Like to some branch of stars we see
Hung in the golden Galaxy.
The bridle bells rang merrily   85
        As he rode down to Camelot:
And from his blazon'd baldric slung
A mighty silver bugle hung,
And as he rode his armour rung,
        Beside remote Shalott.   90

All in the blue unclouded weather
Thick-jewell'd shone the saddle-leather,
The helmet and the helmet-feather
Burn'd like one burning flame together,
        As he rode down to Camelot.   95
As often thro' the purple night,
Below the starry clusters bright,
Some bearded meteor, trailing light,
        Moves over still Shalott.

His broad clear brow in sunlight glow'd;   100
On burnish'd hooves his war-horse trode;
From underneath his helmet flow'd
His coal-black curls as on he rode,
        As he rode down to Camelot.
From the bank and from the river   105
He flash'd into the crystal mirror.
" Tirra lirra," by the river
        Sang Sir Lancelot.

Galaxy : *The Milky Way*

blazon'd baldric : *belt adorned with heraldic emblems*

She left the web, she left the loom,
She made three paces thro' the room,
She saw the water-lily bloom,
She saw the helmet and the plume,
    She look'd down to Camelot ;
Out flew the web and floated wide ;
The mirror crack'd from side to side ;
" The curse is come upon me," cried
    The Lady of Shalott.
      110
      115

Part IV

In the stormy east-wind straining,
The pale yellow woods were waning,
The broad stream in his banks complaining,
Heavily the low sky raining
    Over tower'd Camelot ;
Down she came and found a boat
Beneath a willow left afloat,
And round about the prow she wrote
    The Lady of Shalott.
      120
      125

And down the river's dim expanse—
Like some bold seer in a trance,
Seeing all his own mischance—
With a glassy countenance
    Did she look to Camelot.
And at the closing of the day
She loosed the chain, and down she lay ;
The broad stream bore her far away,
    The Lady of Shalott.
      130
      135

Lying, robed in snowy white
That loosely flew to left and right—
The leaves upon her falling light—
Thro' the noises of the night
        She floated down to Camelot :
And as the boat-head wound along
The willowy hills and fields among,
They heard her singing her last song,
        The Lady of Shalott.

Heard a carol, mournful, holy,
Chanted loudly, chanted lowly,
Till her blood was frozen slowly,
And her eyes were darken'd wholly,
        Turn'd to tower'd Camelot :
For ere she reach'd upon the tide
The first house by the water-side,
Singing in her song she died,
        The Lady of Shalott.

Under tower and balcony,
By garden wall and gallery,
A gleaming shape she floated by,
Dead pale between the houses high,
        Silent into Camelot.
Out upon the wharfs they came,
Knight and burgher, lord and dame,
And round the prow they read her name,
        The Lady of Shalott.

Who is this ? and what is here ?
And in the lighted palace near
Died the sound of royal cheer ;   165
And they cross'd themselves for fear,
    All the knights at Camelot :
But Lancelot mused a little space ;
He said, " She has a lovely face ;
God in His mercy lend her grace,   170
    The Lady of Shalott."

TENNYSON
(1809-1892)

*The questions in group A form a complete set in themselves.
Those in group B may form the basis of a second lesson.*

A

1. The poem is written in four parts. Suggest a title for each.

2. Lines 1-23. Describe the river and the country through
    which it flows.

3. Describe the island of Shalott.

4. What do we learn of the Lady ?

5. The Lady weaves " a magic web with colours gay " (line
    38). Why does the poet not give us more colours in lines
    46-72 ?

6. Why does the passing of Sir Lancelot compel the Lady to
    leave the web ?

7. Lines 73-108. Lines 118-122. Contrast the pictures those
    lines present to you.

8. Lines 168-171. Do you like this ending to the poem ?

    Notes : page 189.

You may omit this page if you wish.

B

Tennyson worked at his poems long and carefully, weighing almost every word in every line he wrote. The following questions ask you to study his workmanship.

CHOICE OF WORDS

1. Stanza 1. Only simple words are used. Consider carefully how much they tell you.

2. Lines 10-11, 127-130. Make plain the full meaning of the verbs in the first description, and of the adjectives in the second.

3. Lines 73-104. Make a list of the words in the description of Lancelot that prepare you for " flashed " (line 106).

4. Lines 34, 105. Why did the poet write " uplands *airy*," and " From the bank and *from the river* " ?

5. Line 143. The swan is said to sing before she dies. Was this thought in the poet's mind ?

THE SOUND OF THE LINES

6. Line 35. Why has the poet introduced three " is " sounds ?

7. Line 52. Why " *surly* village-churls " ?

8. Line 89. What makes you hear the clang of armour ?

9. Line 118. Do you hear the wind ?

10. Lines 145-148. Which vowel sound do you hear most clearly ?

PACE AND RHYTHM

11. Only in one line of the poem, line 21, is there a strong middle pause. What is its effect ?

12. Lines 109-113.

> *She left the web, and left the loom*
> *And made three paces thro' the room,*
> *And saw the water-lily bloom,*
> *And saw the helmet and the plume*
> *And look'd down to Camelot.*

What have we lost ?

13. Lines 66-68. Why do those lines move slowly ?

14. Lines 73-77. Why does this stanza open so abruptly r

15. Contrast the rhythm of lines 28-36 with that of lines 55-63.

16. Is the stanza form better fitted for narrative or description ?

Notes : page 190.

115

THE WIFE OF USHER'S WELL

There lived a wife at Usher's Well,
  And a wealthy wife was she ;
She had three stout and stalwart sons,
  And sent them o'er the sea.

They hadna been a week from her,
  A week but barely ane,
When word came to the carline wife
  That her three sons were gane.

They hadna been a week from her,
  A week but barely three,
When word came to the carline wife
  That her sons she'd never see.

" I wish the wind may never cease,
  Nor fashes in the flood,
Till my three sons come hame to me
  In earthly flesh and blood ! "

It fell about the Martinmas,
  When nights are lang and mirk,
The carline wife's three sons came hame,
  And their hats were o' the birk.

It neither grew in syke nor ditch,
  Nor yet in ony sheugh ;
But at the gates o' Paradise
  That birk grew fair eneugh.

" Blow up the fire, my maidens !
  Bring water from the well !
For a' my house shall feast this night,
  Since my three sons are well."

And she has made to them a bed,
  She's made it large and wide ;
And she's ta'en her mantle her about,
  Sat down at the bedside.

5

10

15

20

25

30

Up then crew the red, red cock,
  And up and crew the grey;
The eldest to the youngest said,
  " 'Tis time we were away."   35

The cock he hadna craw'd but once,
  And clapp'd his wings at a',
When the youngest to the eldest said,
  " Brother, we must awa'.   40

" The cock doth craw, the day doth daw,
  The channerin' worm doth chide;
Gin we be miss'd out o' our place,
  A sair pain we maun bide."

" Fare ye weel, my mother dear!   45
  Fareweel to barn and byre!
And fare ye weel, the bonny lass
  That kindles my mother's fire!"

ANONYMOUS

stout : *strong*	sheugh : *trench*
carline : *old woman*	eneugh : *enough*
fashes : *troubles, storms*	maidens : *servants*
channerin' : *fretting*	Martinmas : *11th November*
birk : *birch (see page* 192)	gin : *if*
syke : *marsh*	byre : *cattle shed*

1. The wife (mistress) of Usher's Well was wealthy. What more do we learn about her?
2. Should the ballad have told us how the sons died?
3. In what mood was the wife when she uttered her wish?
4. Why did the sons return?
5. Whence did they come?
6. Lines 29-32. Why did the mother act thus?
7. Explain lines 47, 48.
8. Did the maker of the ballad believe his story?
9. Why does the poem appeal to twentieth-century readers?

Notes : page 191.

EARL HALDAN'S DAUGHTER

It was Earl Haldan's daughter,
  She looked across the sea ;
She looked across the water ;
  And long and loud laughed she :
" The locks of six princesses
  Must be my marriage fee,   5
So hey bonny boat, and ho bonny boat !
  Who comes a-wooing me ? "

It was Earl Haldan's daughter,
  She walked along the sand ;   10
When she was aware of a knight so fair,
  Come sailing to the land.
His sails were all of velvet,
  His mast of beaten gold,
And " Hey bonny boat, and ho bonny boat !   15
  Who saileth here so bold ? "

" The locks of five princesses
  I won beyond the sea ;
I clipt their golden tresses
  To fringe a cloak for thee.   20
One handful yet is wanting,
  But one of all my tale ;
So hey bonny boat, and ho bonny boat !
  Furl up thy velvet sail ! "

He leapt into the water,   25
  That rover young and bold ;
He gript Earl Haldan's daughter,
  He clipt her locks of gold :
" Go weep, go weep, proud maiden,
  The tale is full to-day.   30
Now hey bonny boat, and ho bonny boat !
  Sail Westward ho ! away ! "

CHARLES KINGSLEY
(1819-1875)

1. In what ways is this poem like a ballad ?
2. For line 29 read, " Set sail, set sail, my seamen ! " Which
  do you prefer ?
  Notes : page 192.

118

PROUD MAISIE

Proud Maisie is in the wood,
  Walking so early ;
Sweet Robin sits on the bush,
  Singing so rarely.

" Tell me, thou bonny bird,   5
  When shall I marry me ? "
" When six braw gentlemen
  Kirkward shall carry ye."

" Who makes the bridal bed,
  Birdie, say truly ? "   10
" The grey-headed sexton
  That delves the grave duly.

" The glow-worm o'er grave and stone
  Shall light thee steady ;
The owl from the steeple sing,   15
  ' Welcome, proud lady ! ' "

SCOTT
(1771-1832)

The stanzas come from Scott's novel, " The Heart of Midlothian ". Madge Wildfire, " a poor maniac ", sings them on her death-bed. " Her voice died away with the last notes, and she fell into a slumber, from which . . . she never would awake ".

1. Earl Haldan's Daughter was called proud with reason. Why *Proud* Maisie ?

2. Kingsley's poem punished pride. Does Scott's ?

3. Do you wish to know more than the poem tells ? Do you wish to have, for example, a picture of the girl ?

4. *Once on a time a girl, walking in a wood, asked a robin red-breast when she would be married. The bird answered that her fate was not marriage, but an early death.*

  What have we lost ?

Notes : page 193.

LA BELLE DAME SANS MERCI

" O what can ail thee, knight-at-arms,
  Alone and palely loitering?
The sedge has wither'd from the lake,
  And no birds sing.

" O what can ail thee, knight-at-arms,
  So haggard and so woe-begone?
The squirrel's granary is full,
  And the harvest's done.

" I see a lily on thy brow
  With anguish moist and fever-dew
And on thy cheeks a fading rose
  Fast withereth too."

" I met a lady in the meads,
  Full beautiful—a faery's child,
Her hair was long, her foot was light,
  And her eyes were wild.

" I made a garland for her head,
  And bracelets too, and fragrant zone;
She looked at me as she did love,
  And made sweet moan.

" I set her on my pacing steed
  And nothing else saw all day long,
For sidelong would she bend, and sing
  A faery's song.

" She found me roots of relish sweet,
  And honey wild and manna-dew,
And sure in language strange she said
  ' I love thee true.'

" She took me to her elfin grot,
  And there she wept and sigh'd full sore,
And there I shut her wild wild eyes
  With kisses four.

" And there she lulléd me asleep,
    And there I dream'd—Ah ! woe betide !
The latest dream I ever dream'd   35
    On the cold hill's side.

" I saw pale kings and princes too,
    Pale warriors, death-pale were they all :
They cried—' La belle Dame sans Merci
    Hath thee in thrall ! '   40

" I saw their starved lips in the gloam
    With horrid warning gapéd wide,
And I awoke and found me here
    On the cold hill's side.

" And this is why I sojourn here,   45
    Alone and palely loitering,
Though the sedge is wither'd from the lake,
    And no birds sing."

KEATS
(1795-1821)

La Belle Dame sans Merci : *The beautiful, pitiless lady*

1. One version of the poem begins : *Ah, what can **ail thee,** wretched wight.* Which do you prefer ?

2. Lines 1-12. What is the season ?

3. Lines 13-16. Can you see the lady ?

4. Line 21. Can you see the steed ?

5. Lines 13-28. What is the season ?

6. Line 29. What is an " elfin grot " ?

7. Line 35. What is suggested by " latest " ?

8. (*a*) Why did the poet make his final stanza so like his first ?
   (*b*) What is the effect of line 48 ?

   Notes : page 193.

COUNT ARNALDOS
(A Spanish Ballad)

Who had ever such adventure,
  Holy priest, or virgin nun,
As befell the Count Arnaldos
  At the rising of the sun?

On his wrist the hawk was hooded,   5
  Forth with horn and hound went he,
When he saw a stately galley
  Sailing on the silent sea.

Sail of satin, mast of cedar,
  Burnished poop of beaten gold—   10
Many a morn you'll hood your falcon
  Ere you such a bark behold.

Sails of satin, masts of cedar,
  Golden poops may come again,
But mortal ear no more shall listen   15
  To yon grey-haired sailor's strain.

Heart may beat, and eye may glisten,
  Faith is strong and Hope is free,
But mortal ear no more shall listen
  To the song that rules the sea.   20

When the grey-haired sailor chaunted,
  Every wind was hushed to sleep—
Like a virgin's bosom panted
  All the wide reposing deep.

Bright in beauty rose the star-fish   25
  From her green cave down below,
Right above the eagle poised him—
  Holy music charmed them so.

" Stately galley ! glorious galley !
    God hath poured His grace on thee !   30
Thou alone may'st scorn the perils
    Of the dread devouring sea.

" False Almeria's reefs and shallows,
    Black Gibraltar's giant rocks,
Sound and sand-bank, gulf and whirl-pool,   35
    All—my glorious galley mocks."

" For the sake of God, our Maker ! "
    (Count Arnaldos' cry was strong.)
" Old man, let me be partaker
    In the secret of thy song."   40

" Count Arnaldos ! Count Arnaldos !
    Hearts I read and thoughts I know—
Would'st thou learn the ocean secret,
    In our galley thou must go."

Translated by JOHN GIBSON LOCKHART
(1794-1854)

Almeria : *town on the south-east coast of Spain*

LORD ARNALDOS

The strangest of adventures
That happen by the sea
Befell to Lord Arnaldos
On the Evening of St. John ;
For he was out a-hunting—   5
A huntsman bold was he ! —
When he beheld a little ship
And close to land was she.
Her cords were all of silver,
Her sails of cramasy ;   10
And he who sailed the little ship
Was singing at the helm :

The waves stood still to hear him
The wind was soft and low ;
The fish who dwell in darkness   15
Ascended through the sea,
And all the birds in heaven
Flew down to his mast-tree.
Then spake the Lord Arnaldos
(Well shall you hear his words !)   20
" Tell me for God's sake, sailor,
What song may that song be ? "
The sailor spake in answer,
And answer thus made he :
" I only tell my song to those   25
Who sail away with me."

JAMES ELROY FLECKER
(*20th Century*)

The Evening of St. John : 23*rd June, Midsummer Eve, a
    day long associated with supernatural happenings. See
    page* 99.
cramasy : *crimson cloth*

1. Which lines in the ballad have no parallel in Flecker's
    poem ?

2. Which do you prefer, the " stately galley " of the ballad
    (line 7) or Flecker's " little ship " (line 7) ?

3. Flecker does not tell us the helmsman was grey-haired.
    Would you have done so ?

4. Do you like the story better with the sailor's song
    ("Count Arnaldos", lines 29-36) or, as Flecker has
    told it, without it ?

5. Compare the ballad, lines 37-44, with " Lord Arnaldos ",
    lines 19-26. Which is the better ending ?

6. Which poem makes you feel more strongly the strangeness
    of the adventure ?

Notes : page 194.

124

SEA FEVER

I must down to the seas again, to the lonely sea and the
   sky,
And all I ask is a tall ship and a star to steer her by,
And the wheel's kick and the wind's song and the white
   sail's shaking,
And a grey mist on the sea's face, and a grey dawn
   breaking.

I must down to the seas again, for the call of the running
   tide
Is a wild call and a clear call that may not be denied ;
And all I ask is a windy day with the white clouds flying,
And the flung spray and the blown spume, and the sea-
   gulls crying.

I must down to the seas again, to the vagrant gypsy life,
To the gull's way and the whale's way where the wind's
   like a whetted knife ;
And all I ask is a merry yarn from a laughing fellow-
   rover,
And quiet sleep and a sweet dream when the long trick's
   over.

JOHN MASEFIELD
(*20th Century*)

Line 1 is usually printed " I must down ", but the poet
approves of your saying " I must go down ", if you choose.

trick : *the spell at the wheel or on the look-out*

Read again " A Wet Sheet and a Flowing Sea " (page 23).

1. The sea has a call for Cunningham's sailors as well as
   for the speaker in " Sea Fever " :
     (*a*) How far is it the same call ?
     (*b*) In what respects is it different ?
2. With which sailor, Cunningham's speaker, or Mr.
   Masefield's, would you choose to be ?
3. What effects have the poets secured from the rhythms
   they have used ?

Notes : page 195.

125

SEMMERWATER

Deep asleep, deep asleep,
Deep asleep it lies,
The still lake of Semmerwater
Under the still skies.

And many a fathom, many a fathom,   5
Many a fathom below,
In a king's tower and a queen's bower
The fishes come and go.

Once there stood by Semmerwater
A mickle town and tall ;   10
King's tower and queen's bower
And the wakeman on the wall.

Came a beggar halt and sore :
" I faint for lack of bread."
King's tower and queen's bower   15
Cast him forth unfed.

He knocked at the door of the herdman's cot,
The herdman's cot in the dale.
They gave him of their oatcake,
They gave him of their ale.   20

He has cursed aloud that city proud,
He has cursed it in its pride ;
He has cursed it into Semmerwater
Down the brant hillside ;
He has cursed it into Semmerwater,   25
There to bide.

King's tower and queen's bower,
And a mickle town and tall;
By glimmer of scale and gleam of fin,
Folk have seen them all.
King's tower and queen's bower,
And weed and reed in the gloom;
And a lost city in Semmerwater,
Deep asleep till Doom.

SIR WILLIAM WATSON
(20th Century)

wakeman : *watchman*　　　　brant : *steep*

THE NECKAN

In summer, on the headlands,
　The Baltic Sea along,
Sits Neckan with his harp of gold,
　And sings his plaintive song.

Green rolls beneath the headlands,
　Green rolls the Baltic Sea,
And there, below the Neckan's feet,
　His wife and children be.

He sings not of the ocean,
　Its shells and roses pale;
Of earth, of earth the Neckan sings,
　He hath no other tale.

He sits upon the headlands,
　And sings a mournful stave
Of all he saw and felt on earth,
　Far from the kind sea wave.

Sings how, a knight, he wander'd
　By castle, field, and town—
But earthly knights have harder hearts
　Than the sea-children own.

127

Sings of his earthly bridal—
  Priests, knights, and ladies gay.
" —And who art thou," the priest began,
  " Sir Knight, who wedd'st to-day ? "—

" —I am no knight," he answer'd ;   25
  " From the sea-waves I come."—
The knights drew sword, the ladies scream'd,
  The surpliced priest stood dumb.

He sings how from the chapel
  He vanish'd with his bride,   30
And bore her down to the sea-halls,
  Beneath the salt sea-tide.

He sings how she sits weeping
  'Mid shells that round her lie.
" —False Neckan shares my bed," she weeps   35
  " No Christian mate have I."—

He sings how through the billows
  He rose to earth again
And sought a priest to sign the cross,
  That Neckan Heaven might gain.   40

He sings how, on an evening,
  Beneath the birch-trees cool,
He sate and play'd his harp of gold,
  Beside the river-pool.

Beside the pool sate Neckan—   45
  Tears fill'd his mild blue eye.
On his white mule, across the bridge,
  A cassock'd priest rode by.

" —Why sitt'st thou there, O Neckan,
  And play'st thy harp of gold ?   50
Sooner shall this my staff bear leaves,
  Than thou shalt Heaven behold."—

But, lo, the staff, it budded !
  It green'd, it branch'd, it waved.
" —O ruth of God," the priest cried out,   55
" This lost sea-creature saved ! "

The cassock'd priest rode onwards,
  And vanish'd with his mule.
But Neckan in the twilight grey
  Wept by the river-pool.   60

He wept : " The earth hath kindness,
  The sea, the starry poles ;
Earth, sea, and sky, and God above—
  But, ah, not human souls ! "

In summer, on the headlands,   65
  The Baltic Sea along,
Sits Neckan with his harp of gold,
  And sings this plaintive song.

ARNOLD
(1822-1888)

1. How far have " Semmerwater " and " The Neckan " a
   common theme ?
2. You have read several old ballads (pages 24, 26, 36, 38,
   40, 116) and have noted that they are story poems,
   and that they tell their stories with little explanation
   or description. Speeches are introduced abruptly.
   They move quickly to their goal and leave the hearer
   or reader to form his own opinion of the deeds they
   narrate. One of their few devices is the repetition of
   phrases and lines.
   In what respects do (a) " Semmerwater ", (b) " The
   Neckan " resemble old ballads ?
3. Had their authors not been known to you, how could
   you have told that these poems belong to modern
   times ?
4. The common ballad-metre is the four-beat, three-beat,
   four-beat, three-beat quatrain of " The Wife of
   Usher's Well " (page 116). How far is it retained in
   (a) " Semmerwater " and (b) " The Neckan " ?
5. Which pictures from these poems are likely to live in
   your memory ?

Notes : page 196.

TEWKESBURY ROAD

It is good to be out on the road, and going one knows
   not where,
   Going through meadow and village, one knows not
      whither nor why;
Through the grey light drift of the dust, in the keen
   cool rush of the air,
   Under the flying white clouds, and the broad blue
      lift of the sky;

And to halt at the chattering brook, in the tall green
   fern at the brink   5
   Where the harebell grows, and the gorse, and the
      fox-gloves purple and white;
Where the shy-eyed delicate deer troop down to the
   pools to drink,
   When the stars are mellow and large at the coming on
      of the night.

O! to feel the warmth of the rain, and the homely
   smell of the earth,
   Is a tune for the blood to jig to, a joy past power
      of words;   10
And the blessed green comely meadows seem all
   a-ripple with mirth
   At the lilt of the shifting feet, and the dear wild cry
      of the birds.

JOHN MASEFIELD
(*20th Century*)

1. What picture do you form of the road?
2. What meaning do you give to " delicate " (line 7)
   " mellow " (line 8) " a-ripple " (line 11)?
3. At what pace would the poet walk?
4. Why is it good to be out on the road? Each stanza
   gives its own answer.
   Notes: page 198.

THE LAKE ISLE OF INNISFREE

I will arise and go now, and go to Innisfree,
  And a small cabin build there, of clay and wattles
    made ;
Nine bean rows will I have there, a hive for the honey-
  bee,
    And live alone in the bee-loud glade.

And I shall have some peace there, for peace comes
  dropping slow,   5
  Dropping from the veils of the morning to where
  the cricket sings ;
There midnight's all a glimmer, and noon a purple
  glow,
    And evening full of the linnet's wings.

I will arise and go now, for always, night and day,
  I hear lake water lapping with low sounds by the
  shore :   10
While I stand on the roadway, or on the pavements
  grey,
    I hear it in the deep heart's core.

WILLIAM BUTLER YEATS
(*20th Century*)

Innisfree : *a Gaelic name which means " the heather-covered
  island "*
wattles : *willow branches*

1. What picture do you form of Innisfree ?
2. Does the poem help you to hear the island, as well as
  see it ?
3. Line 3. Why *nine* bean rows ?
4. Consider stanza 2 carefully. What meaning do you
  give to each line ?
5. Why has the poet determined to go to Innisfree ?
6. Suppose the poet had written in the manner of popular
  songs, " I'm going back to Innisfree ". What would
  you have lost ?

  Notes : page 199.

131

AN OLD WOMAN OF THE ROADS

Oh, to have a little house !
  To own the hearth and stool and all !
The heaped-up sods upon the fire,
  The pile of turf against the wall !

To have a clock with weights and chains   5
  And pendulum swinging up and down !
A dresser filled with shining delph,
  Speckled and white and blue and brown !

I could be busy all the day
  Clearing and sweeping hearth and floor,   10
And fixing on their shelf again
  My white and blue and speckled store !

I could be quiet there at night
  Beside the fire and by myself,
Sure of a bed, and loth to leave   15
  The ticking clock and the shining delph !

Och ! but I'm weary of mist and dark,
  And roads where there's never a house or bush,
And tired I am of bog and road
  And the crying wind and the lonesome hush ! 20

And I am praying to God on high,
  And I am praying Him night and day,
For a little house—a house of my own—
  Out of the wind's and the rain's way.

PADRAIC COLUM
(*20th Century*)

delph : (*or delf*) *pottery*

1. Would you be happy in the life the Old Woman prays for ? Why does the little cottage seem so comfortable and pleasant in the poem ?
2. How will you read the poem ?
3. Like " Sea Fever ", " Tewkesbury Road ", " The Lake Isle of Innisfree ", this is a poem of longing :

  With which speaker in these poems are you most in sympathy ?

Notes : page 200.

132

HOW THEY BROUGHT THE GOOD NEWS FROM GHENT TO AIX

I sprang to the stirrup, and Joris, and he;
I galloped, Dirck galloped, we galloped all three;
" Good speed!" cried the watch, as the gate-bolts
    undrew;
" Speed!" echoed the wall to us galloping through;
Behind shut the postern, the lights sank to rest,   5
And into the midnight we galloped abreast.

Not a word to each other; we kept the great pace
Neck by neck, stride by stride, never changing our
    place;
I turned in my saddle and made its girths tight,
Then shortened each stirrup, and set the pique right, 10
Rebuckled the cheek-strap, chained slacker the bit,
Nor galloped less steadily Roland a whit.

'Twas moonset at starting; but while we drew near
Lokeren, the cocks crew and twilight dawned clear;
At Boom, a great yellow star came out to see;   15
At Duffeld, 'twas morning as plain as could be;
And from Mecheln church-steeple we heard the half-
    chime,
So Joris broke silence with, " Yet there is time!"

At Aerschot, up leaped of a sudden the sun,
And against him the cattle stood black every one,   20
To stare thro' the mist at us galloping past,
And I saw my stout galloper Roland at last,
With resolute shoulders, each butting away
The haze, as some bluff river headland its spray:

And his low head and crest, just one sharp ear bent
    back
                                25
For my voice, and the other pricked out on his track;
And one eye's black intelligence—ever that glance

O'er its white edge at me, his own master, askance!
And the thick heavy spume-flakes which aye and anon
His fierce lips shook upwards in galloping on.   30

By Hasselt, Dirck groaned; and cried Joris, " Stay
    spur !
Your Roos galloped bravely, the fault's not in her,
We'll remember at Aix "—for one heard the quick
    wheeze
Of her chest, saw the stretched neck and staggering
    knees,
And sunk tail, and horrible heave of the flank,   35
As down on her haunches she shuddered and sank.

So we were left galloping, Joris and I,
Past Looz and past Tongres, no cloud in the sky ;
The broad sun above laughed a pitiless laugh,
'Neath our feet broke the brittle bright stubble like
    chaff ;   40
Till over by Dalhem a dome-spire sprang white
And " Gallop," gasped Joris, " for Aix is in sight ! "

" How they'll greet us ! "—and all in a moment his roan
Rolled neck and croup over, lay dead as a stone ;
And there was my Roland to bear the whole weight 45
Of the news which alone could save Aix from her fate,
With his nostrils like pits full of blood to the brim,
And with circles of red for his eye-sockets' rim.

Then I cast loose my buffcoat, each holster let fall,
Shook off both my jack-boots, let go belt and all,   50
Stood up in the stirrup, leaned, patted his ear,
Called my Roland his pet-name, my horse without
    peer ;
Clapped my hands, laughed and sang, any noise, bad
    or good,
Till at length into Aix Roland galloped and stood.

And all I remember is, friends flocking round   55
As I sat with his head 'twixt my knees on the ground;
And no voice but was praising this Roland of mine,
As I poured down his throat our last measure of wine,
Which (the burgesses voted by common consent)
Was no more than his due who brought good news
   from Ghent.   60

Browning
(1812-1889)

pique: *peak of the saddle*   askance: *with a sideways glance*
croup: *back*

The story told in this poem does not come from history. The poet was on board ship when he wrote it, " long enough at sea to appreciate even the fancy of a gallop on the back of a certain good horse, York, then in my stable at home ". It is really another poem of longing, or escape.

1. Why did the poet not tell us what good news he imagined his horsemen to be carrying ?

2. Can you learn from the poem what kind of men the horsemen were ?

3. You will agree that the poet has made his lines gallop. Read the first stanza, marking the beats, thus :

I sprang to the stirrup, and Joris, and he.

Now mark the beats in the following version of stanza 1, and say why these lines do *not* gallop :

I mounted, so did Joris, so did he,
And off we rode upon our horses three.
" Good speed! " cried out the watch, as bolts undrew;
" Speed " echoed from the walls we galloped through.
The gates were shut, and lanterns sank to rest.
'Twas midnight as we galloped forth, abreast.

4. (*a*) Why is it that lines 34, 35 and lines 41-44 sound more slow than most of the others ?
   (*b*) How will you read lines 31-33 ?

5. Compare the picture given in lines 19-24 with that given in lines 37-42.

6. What do these words bring before you—" leaped " (line 19) " fierce " (line 30) lines 49-53, " stood " (line 54) ?

Notes: page 201.

135

THE CAVALIER'S ESCAPE

Trample! trample! went the roan,
  Trap! trap! went the grey;
But pad! *pad*! PAD! like a thing that was mad
  My chestnut broke away.
It was just five miles from Salisbury town,   5
  And but one hour to day.

Thud! THUD! came on the heavy roan,
  Rap! RAP! the mettled grey;
But my chestnut mare was of blood so rare,
  That she showed them all the way.   10
Spur on! spur on!—I doffed my hat,
  And wished them all good-day.

They splashed through miry rut and pool—
  Splintered through fence and rail;
But chestnut Kate switched over the gate—   15
  I saw them droop and tail.
To Salisbury town—but a mile of down,
  Once over this brook and rail.

Trap! trap! I heard their echoing hoofs
  Past the walls of mossy stone;   20
The roan flew on at a staggering pace,
  But blood is better than bone.
I patted old Kate and gave her the spur,
  For I knew it was all my own.

But trample! trample! came their steeds,   25
  And I saw their wolf's eyes burn!
I felt like a royal hart at bay,
  And made me ready to turn.
I looked where highest grew the may,
  And deepest arched the fern.   30

I flew at the first knave's sallow throat;
  One blow, and he was down.
The second rogue fired twice, and missed;
  I sliced the villain's crown,
Clove through the rest, and flogged brave Kate, 35
  Fast, fast, to Salisbury town!

Pad! pad! they came on the level sward,
  Thud! thud! upon the sand;
With a gleam of swords, and a burning match,
  And a shaking of flag and hand: 40
But one long bound, and I passed the gate,
  Safe from the canting band.

THORNBURY
(1828-1876)

The walls of mossy stone (line 20) may be the walls of the
  Cathedral Close, to the south of the city.

1. Do you see, or hear, the Roundheads?

2. (*a*) Lines 1-3, 7-9, 13-15. What does the sound tell you
      about the horses?
   (*b*) Why do lines 13-14 sound especially slow?

3. Though this poem and "How they Brought the Good
      News from Ghent to Aix" are poems of speed, you will
      not read them exactly in the same way. Why?

Notes: page 203.

137

SCHULE IN JUNE

There's no a clood in the sky,
  The hill's clear as can be,
An' the broon road's windin' ower it,
  But—no' for me !

It's June, wi' a splairge o' colour   5
  In glen an' on hill,
An' it's me wad be lyin' up yonner,
  But then—there's the schule.

There's a wude wi' a burn rinnin' through it,
  Caller an' cool,   10
Whaur the sun splashes licht on the bracken
  An' dapples the pool.

There's a sang in the soon o' the watter,
  Sang sighs in the air,
An' the worl' disnae maitter a docken   15
  To yin that's up there.

A hop an' a step frae the windie,
  Just fower mile awa',
An' I could be lyin' there thinkin'
  O' naething ava'.   20

Ay !—the schule is a winnerfu' place,
  Gin ye tak' it a' roon,
An' I've nae objections to lessons,
  Whiles—but in June ?

ROBERT BAIN
(20th Century)

schule : *school*	licht : *light*	windie : *window*
splairge : *splash*	soon : *sound*	fower : *four*
wude : *wood*	disnae : *does not*	ava' : *at all*
caller : *fresh*	docken : *dock leaf*	whiles : *at times*

1. Where is the speaker ?
2. What does he see ?
3. Name some poems he may like.
4. How will you read the last line ?

   Notes : page 204.

AULD LANG SYNE

Should auld acquaintance be forgot
  And never brought to min'?
Should auld acquaintance be forgot
  And auld lang syne?

    For auld lang syne, my dear,   5
      For auld lang syne,
    We'll tak a cup o' kindness yet,
      For auld lang syne.

We twa hae run aboot the braes,
  And pu'd the gowans fine;   10
But we've wandered mony a weary foot
  Sin' auld lang syne.

We twa hae paidl'd in the burn,
  Frae morning sun till dine;
But seas between us braid hae roar'd   15
  Sin' auld lang syne.

And here's a hand, my trusty fiere,
  And gie's a hand o' thine;
And we'll tak' a right guid-willie waught,
  For auld lang syne.   20

And surely ye'll be your pint-stoup,
  And surely I'll be mine;
And we'll tak a cup o' kindness yet,
  For auld lang syne.

BURNS
(1759-1796)

auld : *old*   dine : *dinner-time*
lang syne : *long ago*   braid : *broad*
gowans : *daisies*   fiere : *friend*
paidl'd : *paddled*   pint-stoup : *two-quart measure*
guid-willie waught : *cordial draught (of ale)*
ye'll be your pint-stoup, etc. : *you'll be host to me, and I'll be
    host to you*

1. Why is it that this song, written in Scots, should have
    an appeal in lands far beyond the Solway?

Notes : page 204.

139

NOTES ON THE POEMS

The numbers in brackets after the titles refer to the pages on which the poems appear.

Unlike questions in arithmetic, questions on poetry may frequently have more than one right answer. See page 11, paragraphs 1 and 2.

LEISURE (14)

1. Our quiet watchfulness is to show us the beautiful things in nature that are not seen by the man in a hurry—shy squirrels, lights and shadows in the stream. We are to see all the scene has to give us, Beauty's dancing feet as well as her glance, her full smile of eyes and mouth.

2. Life without leisure misses the full value of what the world has to offer. See note 1.

3. *No time to stand beneath the boughs*
And stare as long as sheep or cows;

    No time to see, when woods we pass,
Where squirrels hide their nuts in grass.

    You will observe that the "beat" falls here on every second syllable.

4. Read the poem with a distinct pause after each couplet.
    Each couplet gives us one thing to think of, or one thing to look at. The pauses between the couplets give us time to think and look. The stanzas are so short that these pauses, or intervals of silence, come close together. Thus we are given a hint of the quiet peace enjoyed by the man who stands and stares.
    The "busy" man declares he has "no time" to stand and stare. The poet's five repetitions of this parrot cry, in lines 3-12, are his way of smiling at "busyness".

5. Possible themes are: Rabbits at play; The thrush listening for worms; Wild ducks; The ripple on a field of corn.
    Examples of couplets:

    > *No time beside a bush to lie,*
    > *While baby finches learn to fly.*

    > *No time to see, when days are dead,*
    > *The first brave primrose raise its head.*

6. Poetry, too, has beauties that are found only by those who are prepared to spend time and care in looking for them. To enjoy it to the full, we must "stand and stare".

141

1. The sights he enjoys—the fishes, the partridge and her brood, the coney—are only for the man who has time to stand and stare. See especially lines 3 and 4.

2. Yes. But he does not state his opinions quite in the same way. He dwells on what the man gains who has leisure ; Davies, on what the man misses who has not leisure.
In his last four lines Breton comes near to Davies's way of putting things. He wrote for an age that had more time than ours, less " busyness " and excitement. He had less need to urge upon his readers the danger of hustle.

3. Each poet states his case in his first couplet and supports it by bringing forward a series of " pictures ". In these we see what the Country Lad gains and what the busy modern man misses.
Have you observed that each poem really consists of one long sentence clinched by a short sentence ?

4. Perhaps those of the partridge and the coney—timid creatures whose ways only a " quiet eye " will see. Lines 15 and 16 of Breton's poem may be at once turned into a Davies " No time " couplet.
Breton's pleasure in the hare hunt and in angling does not accord with Davies's mood.

5. (a) *Who can live in heart so glad*

   As the merry country lad,

   Who upon a fair green baulk

   May at pleasure sit and walk.

   (b) The " beat ", as in " Leisure ", falls on every second syllable. But the rhythm of this poem is " **tum-ti** ", not " **ti-tum** ".
The line in this poem begins with an accented syllable, or " beat ".
The line in the previous poem begins with an unaccented syllable.
You will note there are few pauses here between the couplets.
These lines trip along cheerfully ; those of Davies are slower, more meditative.

NICHOLAS NYE (16)

1. We see a piece of waste ground, either in the corner of an orchard or just outside it. The donkey stands by the thorn-bush. The poet (perhaps as a boy) sprawls on the wall. The drowsy heat has stilled almost all movement.

2. The heavy heat of the weather is referred to in four stanzas. The speaker sprawls half-asleep in the blazing heat. The birds merely twitter. The donkey drowses. The sky is a deep, dark blue. As the boy trudges home, the glow-worm shines and the dew is heavy.

3. He had time and to spare. The scene (stanza 1) has imprinted itself on his memory. He remembers every movement of the donkey. See notes 5 (*b*) and 6.

4. They led similar lonely, unexciting lives. They endured the same blazing heat. See, too, note 6.

5. (*a*) The first half of the poem describes an animal broken, apparently, in spirit and body. The second half dwells on his " gumption ", courage endurance.

   (*b*) The first picture is that visible to the passer-by. The beauty of the second comes to the person who looks long and carefully, " stands and stares ".

6. Perhaps the memories of those sultry, lonely days were so strong that he felt he must describe them. Perhaps he thought with tender gratitude of Nicholas Nye. From the donkey, lonely, neglected, but courageous, he drew courage to face his own loneliness. Sympathy passed between them, and understanding. See lines 29-32.

7. Read it slowly, thoughtfully, " tenderly ". We have an atmosphere of drowsy heat, and little outward movement.
   The short last line to each stanza clearly holds up the pace of the reading. Compare lines 7 and 8 of the poem with

   > *And nobody there my lone to share*
   > *But a donkey, Nicholas Nye.*

   This ending would give an impression of speed and gaiety, foreign to the spirit of the poem.

8. See lines 7, 15, 17, 19, 23, 29, 35, 39.
   Line 23 omits a beat. Compare it with

   > *And once in a while, he seemed to smile.*

   In the poem the smile comes suddenly, unexpectedly, to us, as it did to the boy on the wall. The short line gives it importance, forces us to pause and consider.

LONE DOG (18)

1. Dog and donkey both are lean and lone.

2. Form your own opinion. Lone Dog is proud of his " loneness ". Nicholas Nye suffers without complaint and it takes time for us to discover his courage. Once in a while he smiles. For further animal portraits see pages 52 and 53. See, too, note 8, page 163.

3. The donkey seems more real. The difference is not merely between his silence and the dog's " speech " ; the " thoughts " of the latter are not always such as we imagine a dog having. A doggy rebel might love to bay the moon, but no dog would think of keeping fat souls from sleep. Again, lines 11-12 may express the instincts of a lone dog— his love of the open and freedom—but the actual words of the lines would seem " right " only on the lips of a human wanderer.

4. Nicholas Nye's surroundings help to explain him. They are almost part of him. Lone Dog has no fixed surroundings, no home. He is a wanderer, passing quickly across many scenes. Thus in the poem we are given hints for various pictures—lines 3, 4, 8, 11-12—but all are shadowy.

5. The hissing " s " sounds, the " r ", " u ", and " k " sounds all help to make the line sound bitterly. Listen to the sound of " sharp stone ".

6. To obtain an exact comparison, write out the eight lines in pairs— line 1 of " Lone Dog " followed by line 1 of " Low Dog ", and so with each couple. You will find that in each respect the lines tally.

7. (*a*) The poet has made a stanza that is well fitted to describe the loud courage of the rebel. The " beats ", especially in lines 1-8, sound like barks. The mid-rhymes seem to make those barks still louder. In reading stanzas 1 and 2, " bay the moon ". " Bark " the " beats ", and bring out the rhymes. In stanza 3, lines 1 and 2 should be taken more quietly ; lines 3 and 4 courageously, but not noisily.

   (*b*) Though these lines are so like lines 1-4 of the poem, we must read them in quite another manner. Low Dog is spiritless and lazy. We must avoid loud " barking ", take the lines dully, give the " beats " so little emphasis that they sound almost like the regular ticking of a clock. In discussing the reading of a poem, we should always consider not only the rhythm of the lines, but their meaning as well.

1. In each stanza, lines 1 and 3 have four beats, lines 2 and 4 have three. This is a very common stanza form, especially in ballads. See, for example, " Johnnie Faa " (page 26) " Edom o' Gordon " (page 40) " The Wife of Usher's Well " (page 116). But the ballads rarely have mid rhyme.

2. We have mid-rhyme in the first and third lines—the long lines—of each stanza, though stanza 1 is not wholly regular. In line 3 shall

   we say " húnting " or " hunting´ " ?
   Mid-rhyme does much to give the poem its bright, morning tone. It cuts the long lines in two, so that we are given the impression of quick, happy movement. And the rhymes, coming in rapid succession, convey something of the " merry noise ".
   You will agree that stanza 2 is much more cheerful than this version of it :

   > *The East is bright with golden rays ;*
   > *And darkness it is fled :*
   > *And the trumpet rouses up the Morn*
   > *To leave his idle bed.*

3. Each of us sees his or her own picture. But we shall all paint in bright colours—greens and " golden dyes "—and in every picture there will be lively movement of huntsmen, horses, dogs.

4. Read it in bright, rousing, " bugle " tones, with emphasis on the rhymes.

*   *   *

HAWKE (21)

1. A hawk swoops on its prey. In addition, the word well describes the actual sea-attack. Think of the storm, the French ships running for safety, the English falling upon them and destroying them. A third reason is suggested in note 4 (*a*) below.

2. Line 15. Ships are sunk and ships are captured again and again in naval battles. But the decision to take his fleet without local pilots into the dangerous waters of the bay marks Hawke as a great sailor and a great man. He could have brought forward good reasons for calling off the pursuit. All honour to him that he chose to run the risk of his fleet's destruction and his own disgrace.

3. Each stanza follows the same rhyme-scheme as that of the first.

4. (*a*) The poem as a whole should be read spiritedly. In the first four lines of stanzas 1 and 2 we shall try to convey the roll of great ships at sea. Give the long vowel sound of " swooping " its full value. There is sea-music in it. Listen to the crash of the " r " sounds in line 11.
   In stanza 3, line 17 moves more quickly than those which follow.

(b) In stanzas 1 and 2, lines 5-7 should be taken at greater speed than the others. The rhymes, coming so quickly together, seem to suggest the bustle of the French ports, and the rush of waves and wind and battling ships. In stanza 3, lines 5-7 move more slowly. The furious haste is over.

> *The men that would have mastered us they drummed and marched no more.*

We cannot say the second half of this line quickly, for the poet has chosen words that stay our pace. Pause distinctly at "us" in lines 21, 22, and say the following words proudly.

(c) Note how the last line of each stanza holds the stanza together. When we have said seven lines, our ear demands something more to complete the rhythm. When we have said the eighth, we are content.

5. The prose, in a plain historical way, tells us the story of the time, and by so doing enables us to enjoy the poem more fully. There is satisfaction in learning that Hawke's victory was decisive, that in destroying Conflans' fleet he broke the naval power of France. Our admiration for admiral and sailors is increased when we learn that for six months they had kept watch off Brest, in all weathers, and that they were ready at once to meet the enemy, storm-battered as they were, when he gave them the opportunity. Best of all, we have in the prose the noble words of Hawke to his pilot.

6. The poem to some extent assumes that we know our history, though it tells the story with accuracy. Had the author tried to supply every detail he would not have succeeded in making his story live as he has done. He has chosen his facts, the big facts in the "swoop", and given his attention to them. We see and hear the stir in the French ports (lines 5-7). We hear the breakers in the bay (line 11) see the French fleet fly like a covey of startled birds before the pursuer (line 17) follow it in the gathering darkness through the quicksands (lines 13-15). The rhythm, the fine, brave swing of the lines, causes our pulses to beat faster. We share in the excitement and glory of the day; feel, not as we usually do when we read history, but as the people of 1759 must have felt when the great news reached them.
Now read sentences 3 and 4 of the prose, and immediately afterwards stanza 1 of the poem.

7. The lines given in the question have rhyme, and rhythm of a kind. But read them after stanza 2 of the poem, and note how commonplace and hum-drum they are. Their rhythm has nothing of the sweep of the sea. They give details, but they do not excite us, do not lift us above the level of very plain narrative.
Rhymed prose with a regular rhythm is not poetry, but doggerel.

1. The sailor shows that contempt for danger, that confidence in his ship and his own seamanship, which took Hawke's men to victory.
   Deeds such as those of Hawke made the sea our heritage.

2. Note, further, that the beats are arranged in a " ti-tum " rhythm, that the fifth line of each stanza repeats the fourth, and adds the words, " my boys ", and that the sixth line of each stanza ends in the word " free ". The sailor repeats this word, because life at sea is freedom to him.

3. Read with a feeling of satisfaction. The seadog has left land behind and is again at home. Raise your voice above the storm, let it ring with special heartiness in lines 5, 13, 21, and with pride in lines 23, 24. Here the poem reaches its peak, or climax.

   Compare "Sea Fever", page 125, and notes, page 195.

*   *   *

THE WRAGGLE TAGGLE GIPSIES (24)

1. It is sad or gay according as we sympathise with lord or lady. But it is difficult to sympathise with the lord. He does search for his lady, but the arguments with which he would persuade her to return do not come from a broken heart. The lady seems to think that silk-finished gowns and goose-feather beds may be bought too dearly.
   You will note that the ballad gives her the last word.

2. See "Lone Dog", note 7 (page 144) and note 1 to this poem.
   The rhythm suggests cheerfulness. Each stanza ends with a reckless, jolly line, and most of the other lines skip briskly. Compare stanza 3 with this sober version in regular four- and three-beat lines :

   > *'Twas late at night her lord came home ;*
   > *Asked for his lady then.*
   > *" She's gone," the servants did reply,*
   > *" With ragged gipsy men."*

3. Rhymes are very few. We have mid-rhyme in lines 12 and 15 ; but the place of the end-rhymes is taken by the " O's "—so successfully that at first we are not aware of their absence.

4. See note 1. Let the audience join in the last line of each stanza.
   An excellent way of presenting the story is to turn it into a little play.
   Three speakers are required—the narrator, the lord, the lady.

5. Choose a simple " story " subject and find a good fourth line. Rhymes will not trouble you.
   Here is a possible opening :

   > *'Twas Friday morn when my chum said to me,*
   > *" How would you like to go tramping, O ?*
   > *This night we'll put on our ragged, ragged clothes,*
   > *And we'll off to the harum-scarum campers, O !"*

147

JOHNNIE FAA (26)

1. The stanzas pair as follows:

	Stanza	Stanza	Stanza	Stanza	Stanza
" The Wraggle Taggle Gipsies "	1	2	3	4	9
" Johnnie Faa " . . .	1	5	7	8	6

2. In the English version the lady runs away with the gipsies at once. In " Johnnie Faa " she stays by the gate for six stanzas.
The English version gives four stanzas to dialogue between lord and lady. This the Scottish version omits. There is no hint in the English poem of the defeat of the lady and the punishment of the gipsies. Its sympathies, we feel, are with the runaway. The Scottish ballad leaves us to form our own opinions.

3. The English version does not give a reason. Perhaps the song cast a " glamour ". Perhaps she was tired of the wealth and comfort of her house, and of a lord who rated these things too highly.
The Scottish version leaves us in no doubt. The lady was under a spell. Here is the reason for the full account of what befell by the gate (stanzas 2-6). Note that while the one lady is to sleep in a matter-of-fact " cold open field ", the other will " lie 'neath the moon and the stars ".

4. (*a*) The speaker is the last of the gipsies. You will find that ballads frequently introduce speeches without explanation. See " Annan Water " (page 38).
(*b*) The poem ends well. Much happens between stanza 8 and stanza 9. The gipsy's words permit us to imagine it all. A full account might have led us to sympathise with the unfortunate fourteen, and the ballad does not take sides. Yet, in fairness, it puts forward the gipsy point of view and gives it in the final stanza. Fourteen good men are lost because of the whim of a bonnie lady. Naturally the gipsy says nothing of the spell. The lady to him is merely " wanton " —irresponsible and flighty.

5. You must make your own choice. You may prefer the English poem because of its cheerful swing, its " matter-of-factness ", the triumph of the lady over her rich, but uninspiring lord. Or you may like the " glamour " of the Scottish poem, the sorrow it hints at, the beauty of certain lines and phrases (stanzas 1, 2, 6, 9). Or you may find other and better reasons for yourself.

SNATCHES FROM OLD SONGS (28)

1. *With a fa la la la la.*

2. (a) *I would not be.*   (b) *But I would be.*

   In poetry the presence of accent on a word of one syllable depends to a great extent upon the position of the word in the line. The introduction of " but " in (b) throws " I " into the accented position and " would " into the unaccented.

3. Each stanza will be read in a jolly, care-free manner. No. 1 should perhaps be delivered with the greater gusto.

4. The Sylvans are so hard to rouse that the Satyrs pretend that one or the other must have eaten the drowsy dormouse and contracted the " disease " of sleepiness.

5. The brisk " ti-tum " and occasional " ti-ti-tum " rhythms of Nos. 1 and 2 accord well with their rollicking vigour.
   In No. 3 the Satyrs do not wish to rouse the Sylvans too quickly, before they have had opportunity for mischief. (They do not shake, but tickle them.) The gentle rhythms accord with their quiet, almost stealthy actions. So the " tum-ti " rhythms in No. 4 move

   lightly | as the | little | bee.

*   *   *

A FANCY FROM FONTENELLE (30)

1. *Beauty vanishes ; beauty passes ;*
   However rare—rare it be.   *An Epitaph*—W. de la Mare.

   This is a favourite theme with poets. See in this book " To Daffodils " (page 93) and " Proud Maisie " (page 119).

2. (a) No. Beauty lives long in art. We may still admire lovely things made by Greek sculptors and Egyptian craftsmen many years before the birth of Christ. The beauty of the Bible is undimmed by time and old ballads can still charm us.
   (b) The beauty of the rose endures in the " rhyme " the poet made of it. Beauty may live on in our memories. See " Home Thoughts from Abroad " (page 84) and Wordsworth's " Daffodils " (page 94). Keats said, " A thing of beauty is a joy for ever."

3. The rhythm is cheerful on the whole—

   /   / /   /
  The Rose in the garden slipped her bud;

but not so light-hearted as that of " The Priest and the Mulberry Tree ". You will find that while the first two stanzas move easily, the third cannot be said so quickly. In particular note how speed is slowed down by three beats coming together in

    /   / / /   /
  That the leaves of the blown Rose strewed the ground,

and that difficulties of pronunciation hold up the fourth line of the stanza. We cannot say " raked them gently " with speed.

This poem provides a fine example of a poet's skill in making his lines trip lightly or move slowly as he wishes. Remember how the pace of the first two stanzas of " Hawke " (page 21) grew more slow and proud in the last lines of stanza 3.

4. Note 3 tells you. Read lines 1-8 with the joy and pride of youth, lines 9-14 " gently ".

     *   *   *

SEPTEMBER (31)

1. She is entirely happy, like the poet of " November Days " (page 45). There is no thought in her stanzas of winter and the short life of lovely things.

2. September is " merry " and " bountiful ", a season of red apples and " ripe-brown " nuts. Its flowers are " gorgeous ", its skies are clear.

3. (*a*) The lines in the question are written in a flat, monotonous rhythm. The fifth line in particular is very slow and hard to say. Compare the gaiety of

  And the sun looks through
  A clearer blue

with the heaviness of

  Through blue skies the sun shines bright.

The poet expresses her happiness in lines that move brightly and are spoken with ease.

(*b*) The lines in the question are all of one length and the arrangement of the rhymes is commonplace. But the poet bursts suddenly into short lines, with rhymes that come hard one after the other. We feel she has so much to tell us that she cannot pause in her song of praise. Note, too, the repetition of line 13 in line 14. A similar light-hearted effect was produced by the mid-rhymes of " The Hunt is Up ". See note 2, page 145.

4. See note 3 (*b*). The whole poem will be said with happy enthusiasm. In the short lines the rhythm and the rhymes will be clearly marked, and the pace quickened, ever so little.

150

1. Lines 16-22. Lines 27-28. There we have the essentials of the story, the " pride " and the " fall ".

2. But for the mare's tractability, there had been no story.

3. Pride goes before a fall.

4. We are to smile—at the absurd, but not dangerous position in which the curate finds himself ; at the abrupt end to his " fond reverie " ; at the knowledge that he has brought his mishap upon himself.

5. The curate has more dignity to lose and his fall is more amusing. A pompous person and a schoolboy step into a puddle. At which do we laugh more heartily?

6. We may take two hints—one from the cheerful rhythm, the other from the conversational, almost gossiping tone of the first words, " Did you hear ".

7. Further promises come from the word " merrily " in line 2, from the description of the mare, and from the simple rhyme scheme.

8. This rhythm is well fitted to a story of rapid, cheerful movement. Compare " The Wraggle Taggle Gipsies " (page 24).

9. Read it at a good swinging pace. Bring out the rhymes. But do not emphasise the " beats ". The curate would trot, rather than gallop. For examples of galloping poems see " Lochinvar " (page 87) and " How They Brought the Good News from Ghent to Aix " (page 133).

*   *   *

ROUNDABOUTS AND SWINGS (34)

1. We are not told, but we can infer from his view of life that he is neither so young as to expect " millions ", nor so old as to be out of love with his fate. He is a " cheery cove " with a fairly long experience. See lines 11-16.

2. See note 1. The gipsy is in the " September " of his life. He has reaped his harvest of experience, and has taken to reflecting on what he has seen. " An early morn in April " is full of eager hope. It would not prepare us for the quiet contentment of his outlook, his " sooth of lose-and-win ".

" After tea " is the September of the day, when we have time to enjoy life, and to think of what the day has brought us.

151

3. The lurcher looks " wise as Solomon ", jogging in the dust beside his master (line 8). The thump on the foot-board (line 19) may be a hint to him to keep close, though, certainly, it may be a signal to the horse to move on.

Line 7. All good lurchers are lean. Fat dogs catch no hares.

4. The spirit of the poem—of roundabouts and swings—is perfectly maintained. The " up-and-down " note of the bird suggests that the balance of life, its lose-and-win, will be kept. The day is passing, but the sunset is gold-dust.

5. " Leisure " and " The Country Lad " are poems of quiet observation and reflection, in the spirit of " Roundabouts and Swings ".

6. " The Hunt is Up " is a morning poem, with all the high spirits of the sunrise. " Nicholas Nye " is heavy with the heat of a stifling afternoon. The Priest rode up to his Mulberry Tree on a cheerful forenoon in autumn. When you think again of " Roundabouts and Swings ", you will recall the quiet and beautiful September evening painted in lines 19-22.

7. This is the quieter poem. It has something of an evening air, something of the conversation of men whose work is over for the day. The long line with its seven steady beats :

What's lost upon the roundabouts we pulls up on the swings,

and the long eight-line stanza are well fitted to express its quiet philosophy.

In the jerky version of lines 9-12 the " September " spirit has been lost. We have no longer time to stand and talk in the peace of the evening.

*   *   *

GET UP AND BAR THE DOOR (36)

In old times, before turnips were a field crop, farmers were compelled to kill off their surplus cattle in October or November through lack of suitable winter food for them. The women of the house had a very busy time preserving beef for use in the months to come. The " puddings " of the ballad are a kind of sausage.

1. The second " chapter " begins with the arrival of the strangers in stanza 5.

Stanzas 1-4 merely set the scene. The poet rightly supplies only the necessary details—the circumstances of the " paction ". His second " chapter " is longer, because he is mainly interested in the humour of the situation when the silent couple are faced with the problem of their uninvited guests. But in this part, too, he omits unnecessary talk.

2. Stanzas might be inserted as follows :

between lines 12 and 13, to give a fuller account of the quarrel ;
between lines 16 and 17, to tell how the long hours passed in the house ;
between lines 20 and 21, to describe the entry of the " gentlemen " ;
between lines 24 and 25, to show how the visitors took their silent reception.

152

But those additions would make the story neither more plain nor more
humorous. They might, indeed, weaken the story, by slowing it down,
for the speed with which it is told is one of its great merits. A longer,
"padded" poem could not be so gay. It could not imitate the goodwife
and "skip".

3. Here, by way of example, is a stanza to follow line 24 :

> *" A deaf goodwife and a dumb goodman*
> *I ne'er before did see,*
> *Wi' an open door, and a deein' fire,*
> *And puddings in the bree."*

The strangers might have paused to say this, but the ballad-maker
took them straight to the puddings.

4. The one "gentleman" speaks to the other. Again the ballad omits
details which the hearer or reader may easily supply. You may have
noted similar omissions in "The Wraggle Taggle Gipsies" (page 24)
and "Johnnie Faa" (page 26). See, too, "Annan Water" (page 38) and
note 2 on that poem (page 153).

5. The wife deserves to win. Her husband is to blame for the quarrel
She was busy and he was not. The barring of the door was clearly his.
duty.
Note that the goodwife says nothing spiteful in her victory, but preserves
her good humour to the end.

6. Like "The Wraggle Taggle Gipsies", this is a homely or "domestic"
ballad. Violence and death have no place in either. Both show that
life in the old days was not always tragic, that men and women could
laugh then, as now.

*   *   *

ANNAN WATER (38)

1. The hero speaks.

2. Ballads often introduce speeches in this manner, without the explanations
to which we are accustomed. See "The Wraggle Taggle Gipsies",
"Johnnie Faa", "Get up and Bar the Door", "Edom o' Gordon"
(page 40) and "The Wife of Usher's Well" (page 116). An introductory
phrase may be used, as in "The Wraggle Taggle Gipsies", line 11, but
examples are not nearly so numerous as they are in modern books. Ballads
were made hundreds of years ago, by and for people who knew little or
nothing of books. They were for long recited, not printed, and the reciter
would mark the change from narrative to direct speech by voice, facial
expression, gesture. This abrupt method of story-telling certainly

153

makes for speed and vigour. For example, the hero would not seem so gallant and forceful, if between stanza 5 and stanza 6 we had to read something like this :

> He has loupen down upon the bank,
>   And scanned the water, dark and broken ;
> Then hastened to the boatman's door,
>   And straight to him these words has spoken :

The great ballads left ordinary details to the imaginations of their hearers.

3. We are told nothing, apart from the fact that the lady was " bonnie ". See notes 4 and 9, below.

4. This poem, like ballads in general, tells a story, and tells it barely. Descriptions are not introduced for their own sake. It is necessary for our understanding of the story that we should know something of the hero's nature (lines 6-8) and something of the force of the river (lines 23, 29-30). A description of the hero's appearance is not necessary, and, therefore, is not given. Note that adjectives are used sparingly. See note 9, below, and compare note 2 on " Edom o' Gordon " (page 155).

5. He had sworn to meet his lady (line 25). The poem, again in the ballad manner, does not enter into details.

6. Stanza 3. You will have found that nouns, not **adjectives**, are the descriptive words. See notes 4 and 8 (last lines).

7. We admire his faithfulness and his courage—the simple, manly virtues that appealed to the people who first made and listened to ballads.

8. The knowledge that the hero is doomed comes to us slowly. In the first stanzas we learn of his devotion to his lady and his firm determination to carry out his intention. His impetuosity is revealed in lines 7-20. Only when his devotion and impetuosity are faced by the drumlie stream which the boatman dares not cross, do we realise what the end is to be. Note how quietly the description of the river is worked up in lines 23, 27-28, before it is placed full before us in lines 29-30. Note, too, the power of lines 31-32. No wealth of adjectives could have told us so much.

9. It is the very simplicity that moves us. The maker of the ballad might have added much to his poem in the attempt to make it more pathetic. He might have described at length the courage of the hero and the wondrous beauty of his lady. He might have told us of the hopeless struggle in the river, of Annie's grief, perhaps of her early death. He has given us, instead, lines 35 and 36. He has trusted to our imaginations, stirred by the story, to supply details. Further, he has said nothing of his own feelings. His place is to tell the story, quietly. He leaves the pathos of his tale to make itself felt.

154

EDOM O' GORDON (40)

1. His sympathies are with the lady and her children. He speaks of the false Gordon, the bloody butcher, his foul heart's blood. He deals him speedy punishment, which is not in keeping with the actual facts of history. Yet, in the main, he is true to the ballad tradition, in that he tells his story quietly, without personal comment. He is interested in his tale, rather than in the feelings of his audience, and he does not set himself to wring tears from the eyes of his hearers. Compare " Johnnie Faa ", " Annan Water ", " The Wife of Usher's Well " (pages 26, 38, 116).

2. The adjectives are there, not because the ballad maker wished to indulge in descriptive work, but because he felt they gave additional force to his narrative. The fresh, young beauty of the girl makes us feel more keenly the pity of her death.

3. Yes. The blood-lust leaves him at the sight of the dead girl. This transformation of Gordon from a monster to a man whom we can understand, with whom we can even sympathise, is one of the most memorable things in ballad poetry. We can think of no other words to take the place of those he uses in stanzas 21-23. Yet they are, in themselves, all simple words that are part of everyday speech. As the ballads were made to be spoken, their makers naturally chose words from the language of the people. And such words, when nobly used, have power that no elaborate, " book " words can rival.

   Compare the last stanzas of " Annan Water ", and stanzas 4-6 of " The Wife of Usher's Well ".

4. Decide for yourself.

   A modern poet might prefer to end his story at line 116, believing that the punishment of the evil-doers can take away nothing from the horror of their deed, and that after the burning of the castle all other happenings seem of little importance.

   But the ballad was made at a time when men believed that evil should be punished. And even to-day some of us may find satisfaction in reading those twelve lines of vengeance.

*　　　　*　　　　*

A SONG and NOVEMBER DAYS (45)

1. Dixon uses quiet colours : browns, yellows, greys. He tells of a dull day in late autumn or early winter, a sky heavy with clouds through which the sun glints wildly. In the foreground of our picture are the stream, swelling and dark from recent rains, the tattered growths on its banks, the overhanging willows with the silver of their leaves fast turning yellow. Taller trees stand out, naked and dark, against the sky. The thistle that grew so proudly on the top of the bank has lost its summer bravery. Its white head and grey stalk tell the same quiet story of

decay. Only in one place are the soft tones of the picture broken—where the robin shows his breast of new-found red, as he sings his autumn song.

1. It is less easy to make one picture from "November Days". The poet is looking at a district, rather than a single scene. He may, indeed, be describing more than one day, be bringing together in this list of his "loves" all that have given him joy in those bright days that hold off winter. We may see a cottage nestling in a grove of trees and protected by them from the light wind that blows down the faded leaves. The smoke curls upward; the sparrow on the roof chirps gaily in the gentle sunlight; the pigeons sit round their cote; the cock crows cheerfully on the dung-hill. In the distance, away from the sheltered homestead, the wind is strong enough to drive the mill-sails and to shake down the ripe acorns to the pigs.

Clare's picture is brighter than Dixon's. We feel that there is still warmth in the air and blue in the sky, though he makes little use of colour.

2. In "A Song" there is movement in the stream, and, perhaps, in the sky, but the poet does not dwell upon it. The year, as he sees it, has halted for a moment, a few steps from the journey's end. Compare the stillness of the scene with that of the September evening in "Roundabouts and Swings" (page 34).

Study Clare's pictures, and you will find that only one—that of the pigeons—is motionless. Consider to how many of his "loves", besides the gust, the word "fitful" may be applied. It may describe the shaking of the twig, the chirping of the sparrow, the crowing of the cock, the pattering of the acorns, the scrambling of the pigs. Clare finds his pleasure in the cheerful movement of the scenes he describes.

3. In "A Song" we hear only the clear, fine notes of the robin above the dull roll of the water. In "November Days" the sounds are lively: the sparrow's chirp suggests Spring, the crowing of the cock is cheerful, and not uncheerful are the voices of the grunting pigs.

4. See above. Clare obviously delights in the cheerfulness of his scenes. Dixon does not tell us he is happy, but had he not found pleasure in his scene, he could not have described it so beautifully and tenderly. He accepts the fast approach of winter without grieving, and tells us faithfully what he sees. As we read his poem, we are able to look at the season with his eyes, and to enjoy with him its peace and beauty.

5. Those who know the country will agree that both poets present true pictures. You must decide for yourself which is the more pleasing.

6. The chief reason why "A Song" sounds less lively is that its theme is less lively. See "Lone Dog", note 7, page 144.

"A Song" has four two-syllabled, or "double", rhymes—"willow", "yellow"; "bushes", "rushes"; "older", "moulder"; "barer", "rarer". Double rhymes in themselves often make for cheerfulness.

(Read "The Fifteen Acres" (page 90) and, if you can, "The War Song of Dinas Vawr ", in Book III). But the arrangement of " double " and " single " rhymes in " A Song " helps to hold up the movement. The easy flow of lines 1 and 2 is interrupted by line 3, and that of lines 4 and 5 by line 6.

It is interesting to note how the introduction of a double rhyme would slow down the speed of " November Days ".

Compare with the original opening lines this modified version :

> *I love the fitful gust that shaketh*
> *The casement all the day,*
> *And from the glossy elm-tree taketh*
> *The faded leaves away.*

7. You will read " A Song " quietly and thoughtfully. In " November Days " you will bring out the cheerfulness the poet feels in the brisk, lively movement around him.

*   *   *

LATE AUTUMN and WINTER (47)

1. The poems describe the same period of the year. Both put quiet pictures before our eyes. They even speak of the same things—the dead thistles and the robin. Each has a still, calm rhythm. Neither grieves over the passing of summer. See too, note 3 below.

2. All are good, because they are true and vivid. " Blue-glancing " is an exact description of the plough-share as it appears now and again through the plants and the earth that it turns over. The thistles are long and lean. They have lost their firm coats of summer leaves. Their white down is scattering. They stand stiff and straight as blind men. Look carefully at the next robin you see, and note how well " slant-legged " describes his stance. Moreover it is a new word to us and makes us think of the bird, makes us see him, as more common adjectives— " friendly ", for example, or " lively "—fail to do. The poet makes us see what we had seen before, but did not know we had seen.

3. This is not an easy question. It is not always easy to explain our own thoughts, to say nothing of those of another. But the ploughing scene is not merely wintry. The farmer ploughs from autumn to spring, and, even in winter, ploughing foretells the coming of spring. The thistles decay gradually. We are not aware of their actual change from summer to winter. The robin, however, spends his summer away from the homes of men, and his breast in that season is dull in colour. When he returns suddenly to our sight, with his new, bright coat, we are driven to think of the approach of winter. Note that the final picture is that of the robin in " A Song " also.

4. Perhaps by the dumb stillness of his picture. The wind is " frozen ", and " creeps " like the stream. The dull monotony of the mill-wheel's sound serves only to make the silence more silent. The only living thing is a bird—mourning for her dead mate.

157

5. A short poem may be as perfect as one of many lines, even as a small picture may be as beautiful as a large one. Here, as in " A Song " and "The Fallow Deer at the Lonely House " (page 52) we are not shown every detail of the scene, but the details which interested the poets. Longer poems might well have been less moving. Mr. Young's thoughts of winter might not have come to us so suddenly and memorably after many stanzas, and Shelley's poem expanded to greater length might not have seemed so bare and still.

*   *   *

THE STORM-BLAST and SEA-WEED (48)

1. Like a tyrant, the blast compels obedience to its will.

2. " Swift " would do most to complete the description.

3. We see two men running a deadly race. They are so close that the shadow of the pursuer stretches beyond the feet of his prey. The fugitive's head, bent forward to escape the blow, offers a vivid comparison with the sloping masts of the ship—a comparison you are not likely to forget.

4. (a) Speed is suggested by the picture of a winged pursuer (line 3) that " chases " the ship.

The fleeing ship looms up before us in line 5.

Lines 5-10 form one sentence. Read lines 5-8 and note the effect of the rhymes—" prow ", " blow ", " foe "—in thrusting us forward to the main clause—" the ship drove fast ". We cannot pause earlier.

Line 9 gives us really two short lines, each of four one-syllabled words, with the bold rhymes—" fast ", " blast "—following, the one on the heels of the other, like pursuer on pursued.

(b) The pursuer is not only swift, but furious. Think of the words the poet uses—" Storm-blast ", " tyrannous ", " struck ", " chased ", " yell ", " blow ", " roared ".

There is fury in the sound of many lines. Note the " r " effects in lines 1-3, 6-9. Similarly the " s " and " st " sounds make us hear the lash of the tempest. Note particularly lines 3-4, 9.

Compare " Sea-weed " ; stanza 3, especially, for " r "; and stanza 2 for " s " and " sh "—which make us hear the waters upon the rocks. Now, hear for yourself how the speed and the fury have gone out of this prose version of lines 5-10 of " The Storm-blast " :

Aye we fled southward, for the blast roared loudly and the ship drove fast before it, with sloping masts and dipping prow, like a man who, pursued with yell and blow, still treads upon the shadow of his foe, and bends his head forward.

The poet's rhythm, his rhymes, his arrangement of his ideas and his words, all play their part.

158

5. His choice of places emphasises the wide extent of the storm. "Gigantic" is a good descriptive word. It means " giant-like " in size, as well as in strength.

6. The poem forms one sentence. As in lines 5-10 of " The Storm-blast " we cannot rest until we read the last line. But here the effect produced is not so much one of fast movement as of unceasing movement.

7. Evidently we must retain stanza 1, which contains the subject and the predicate of the sentence, and stanza 4, without which we have not the full expression of the poet's thought—that after storm comes peace.

8. See note 5, above. The Storm-wind would not appear so powerful, if we did not hear of his far-stretching dominion. Moreover the omission of stanzas 2 and 3 would destroy much of the majesty of the poem. Listen to the rhythm of the first stanza, and you will feel that it must be repeated more than once before you are satisfied.

9. "Atlantic ", " gigantic ", " scourges ", " surges ". See question 10.

10. It has lost all the grandeur of the storm-music, has become common-place and hum-drum. The short lines are a very important part of the stanza-form. They suggest something of the movement of the waves and the sound of their dash upon the rocks. They compel us to read slowly and with power.

11. The fourth stanza must be taken more quietly than the others. The violence of the storm is dying down. The toiling surges are gradually finding repose, and the sea-weed drifts to shelter.

12. You must see your own pictures.
The Storm-blast may be a great bird, or, perhaps better, a great winged fiend, pursuing a solitary victim, venting all its hate upon one ship.
The Storm-wind need not be winged. We do not think so much of his speed as of his power and the extent of his sway. He may be a giant scourging the whole ocean in his anger.

13. Study the preceding notes.

*　　*　　*

THE WITCHES' CHARM (50)

The principal scene in " The Masque of the Queens " was the House of Fame, and the principal characters were twelve famous queens of history. But first was presented, by way of contrast, an " ugly hell " whence came forth the enemies of Fame—Ignorance, Malice, and the rest—in the guise of witches " with a kind of hollow and infernal music . . . all with spindles, timbrels, rattles, or other instruments, making a confused noise with strange gestures ". They began to dance, but suddenly discovered that their chief or " dame " had not joined them. To summon her they chanted the charm you have read. On its conclusion, she "entered to them, naked-armed, barefooted, her frock tucked, her hair knotted, and folded with vipers; in her hand a torch made of a dead man's arm, lighted, girded with a snake".

1. The colours are black and red. See lines 7 and 8.

2. The creatures of ill-omen are gathered together, under an unearthly, a "wicked" sky. All is ready for the entrance of the dame, the high priestess of the witches. We feel that deeds of darkness are about to be performed, that there is evil in the air. The poet has created what is sometimes called an "atmosphere" of evil. So we may speak of the atmosphere of "The Country Lad" as one of peace, of that of "The Hunt is Up" as one of cheerfulness, of that of "Roundabouts and Swings" as one of September reflection.

3. (a) The mid-rhymes make the lines run more furiously. We imagine that at each rhyme the dancers make some wild gesture. Instead of lines 1-8, read these :

> *The owl is afield, the bat, and the toad,*
> *And so is the cat-a-mountain;*
> *The ant and the slug sit both in a hole,*
> *And the frog peeps out o' the fountain;*
> *The dogs they do bark, and the timbrels play,*
> *The spindle is now a-turning;*
> *The moon it is red, and the stars are gone,*
> *But all the sky is a-burning.*

You will agree that much of the excitement has vanished.
(b) The changes in rhythm at lines 9 and 13 emphasise the wild disorder of the dance. No doubt the poet felt that his witches were creatures too "confused" and "strange" to dance and speak to one rhythm for any length of time.
Note, too, that the subject-matter of the poem is presented in three parts. Lines 1-8 describe the evil, eerie scene. Lines 9-12 move more quickly, showing, as they do, the hideous preparations of the witches and their growing excitement. Lines 13-18, the fastest of all, call for the dame in furious, frenzied speech.

*   *   *

UP IN THE MORNING EARLY (51)

1. Choose for yourself. Note three methods used by the poet of making the cold felt : first, that of direct description in lines 5 and 6 ; second, that of suggesting its grimness by describing its effects on the birds (lines 9-10) third, that of repetition—of line 4, and stanza 1.

2. Stanza 1 is the more cheerful. The snow on the hills (line 3) may be far
   away, but the east wind and the snow-drift are very near. We may
   imagine the speaker in the first stanza safe under cover, even beneath the
   blankets, and in stanza 2 preparing shortly to face the storm.

3. The poet's dislike of winter. Try to make your reading hint at the
   shivering discomfort of the season. Make good use of the " r " and " s "
   sounds in the poem, and the thin, cold " i " sounds in line 9. You may,
   perhaps, suggest a shudder in the second syllables of the rhyme words,
   " early ", " fairly ", " sairly ", " sparely ".

4. Read stanza 4 with more feeling, with a greater sense of discomfort. The
   words are an exact repetition of lines 1-4, but before you come to them you
   have thought of the miseries of lines 5-12.
   The poet repeated the stanza to drive home his meaning. You must
   drive it home in your reading.

*   *   *

THE FALLOW DEER AT THE LONELY HOUSE (52)

1. Only to a lonely house would the deer venture to come so close. A
   " sheet of glistening white " stretches from the walls.

2. " Think " (line 5). We picture elderly people sitting by the fire. There
   is quiet in the house, as there is out of doors.

3. Perhaps " tiptoe " (line 12). The deer is all a-quiver, ready to flee at
   the smallest sound or movement.

4. See preceding notes. (a) The room is warm in the light of fire and lamp.
   The curtains drawn against the night leave but a chink for wondering
   eyes.
   (b) Snow covers the ground. There is probably a gleam from the
   stars, but the scene is not bathed in moon-light. The house is a dark
   shape. In the shaft of lamp-shine stands the deer.
   Both scenes are still and silent.

5. The poet sees, or imagines, the eyes " aglow ". They bring the deer to
   his mind, and from his knowledge of it he pictures the eyes " wondering ",
   " tiptoe (see note 3) " fourfooted ", the eyes of an animal, at whose
   thoughts man can only guess.

6. Had the poem opened with the words, " A fallow deer ", it would have
   at once become a matter-of-fact statement. The poet is not merely
   recording an event ; he is showing us how he is affected by it. He
   knows the strange visitor is a deer, but he *feels* that it is a creature from
   afar, almost from another world than his. " One without " gives us
   the clue to his feeling.

7. See note 4 on " Winter " (page 157). Shelley *tells* us how still it is,
   makes us feel that it is hard and cold. Hardy *hints* at the stillness in
   his description of the people (lines 5 and 6) and in that of the deer
   (lines 11 and 12).

161

3. Read the stanza, omitting line 4, and you will find that its rhythm is less appropriate. It is jerky and almost conversational. The stanza the poet has given us is slow and quiet.

Without line 4 the statement becomes matter-of-fact. The repetition of the first line makes us, in some way, more conscious of the presence of the deer. We might almost say that the house is held by its gaze as in a spell.

Compare the effect of line 10 in stanza 2.

9. You will read the poem quietly and rather slowly. You are in the house, and loud tones would startle the shy visitor. But your tones will not be dull. You, too, are "tiptoe". It is exciting to know that the deer looks in upon you from only a few feet away.

*　　　*　　　*

MILK FOR THE CAT (53)

1. Curtains are drawn at five o'clock, either at the beginning or towards the end of winter.

2. It is a comfortable house, and fairly large. The poet speaks of *all* the neat curtains, tells us that tea is "brought" (by servants) hints at a blazing fire (line 6) and refers to "the great arm-chair" (line 34).
The old ladies, who "stroke their silk", and the children, who "wriggle and laugh", seem to be happy and at peace with things. But the poet's interest is in the eager, unsatisfied cat. The people are dim figures in the background of his picture.

3. This is not a Lonely House. So far as we can judge, it is an ordinary house, lived in by ordinary people. See note 2. Against this background the poet sets the little black cat, living her own life, going her own way, silent and self-centred.

4. Lines 17 and 18 make stronger the contrast referred to in note 3. The human beings have no conception of the cat's "passion" for milk. Tea to them is a meal. Milk to her is something far more—a thing to love (line 24), a religion (line 31).

5. In lines 21, 22 the poet is making us see things with the cat's eyes. The ladies and children are as gods above her. They can confer happiness at will. They dwell in the high, unknown "table-land". At last from the "clouds" (of linen) comes the one thing the cat knows—the saucer, shining, round, beautiful, adorable, smaller than, but not unlike, the other circle that shines upon the roofs at night.

6. The cat is not greedy. Her love of milk is a far higher thing than mere gluttony. It is a devotion, a reverence, almost. The drops are "holy". In lines 29-31 we are asked to live the cat's life. To us she is not long in drinking a saucerful of milk. But to her this joy is timeless; she does not think of it beginning or ending. We may think of many things as we eat and drink. But milk has become her whole world. The whiteness of it is without limit or even shape.

7. After the excitement, the rapture, the cat relaxes, " sinks back into the night " of her normal, sleepy existence. She no longer wants anything, but is content to pull herself into a ring and drowse. The satisfaction of her craving has " defeated " her, put her eager, seeking brain to sleep.

8. It is very difficult, even for poets, to describe animals faithfully, because of the temptation to assign human qualities to them. Lone Dog becomes almost a human rebel, a mouthpiece for human longings for freedom. Nicholas Nye remains a donkey—a donkey seen by a sympathetic and understanding poet. If he did not actually " smile " (line 23) his quiet endurance said all that a smile could say.
The Fallow Deer remains " four-footed ", " tip-toe ", the strangest of all the four beasts, because the poet has not tried to explain away its mystery.

The Little Black Cat is described by a poet who knows her very well. You will agree that his picture of her in lines 1-20, 25-28, is taken from life. But in lines 21-24, 29-32, he tries to look into the cat's brain, to see the saucer with her eyes, as it were, and taste the milk with her tongue. He has tried hard not to give her human feelings. It is for each reader to decide whether he has succeeded in imagining how a cat feels.

9. (a) The prose gives a good " outside " view of the cat's behaviour. But she does not come to life as she does in the poem. The prose observes the cat ; the poem sympathises with her. Compare, particularly, prose, lines 7-14 and poem, lines 21-36.

(b) The prose tells a barer story. It omits many of the poem's pictorial words and vivid phrases, e.g., " the neat curtains ", " bright green eyes ", " one breathing, trembling purr ".

(c) The prose is more hurried. The poem gives us leisure to " stand and stare ", to note every motion of the cat.

(d) The poem's stanza structure, and its use of rhyme and rhythm make it more easily memorised. Note that each stanza is really a paragraph, dealing with one step in the narrative, and that to the majority of the stanzas there comes an emphatic conclusion in a short line with a pronounced rhyme. Note, for example, how strong is the statement made by the four simple words of line 8, coming after the long lines 5-7. Compare the simplicity of line 32. Compare the brevity of line 16, and listen to the purring sound of it.

(e) The poet makes use of rhythm in a manner the prose can not imitate. Contrast the jerky rhythm of stanzas 3 and 4, in which the cat is strained and restless, with the soft, satisfied ease of stanza 7.

1. The North-easter blows from the Scandinavian and German shores that were the homes of our Norse and Saxon ancestors.
It drives our ships out into the Atlantic—as it drove those of our fore-fathers—on worthy enterprises.

2. The references in the passage, lines 17-44, are to the eastern counties of England. See, among others, lines 6, 17, 18.

3. The sports are fishing, shooting, hunting, skating. Their call is for the manly, out-of-doors virtues—endurance, resourcefulness, fitness.

4. Listen to lines 25-28. But you may prefer others.

5. You will find on examination that it is possible to arrange the lines in quatrains (stanzas of four lines). But you will also find that by this arrangement something of the sweep and force and speed of the poem would be destroyed. The North-east wind does not blow in " stanzas ". It does not pause between one activity and the next. It drives over the whole country, " through the snow-storm hurled ".

6. See notes 1 and 3. The poet considers that the North-easter toughens the people of our islands, fits them for high duties and sends them forth to seek them. His last line is the climax to the passage that begins in line 45 with " the luscious South-wind ". Observe how scorn and enthusiasm are mingled at first (lines 45-60). Then comes the peroration, or conclusion (lines 61-68) in which he states most strongly what he feels most deeply, and ends with the strongest line of all.

7. See notes 5 and 6. Read the poem, generally, with vigour, to show that you believe in what you are saying. Take your cue from the opening lines. But observe that you have opportunities for much more than noise. Note the changes in force, pace, expression, demanded by the various sections of the poem—the cheerful welcome of lines 1-8, the contempt hinted at in lines 9-14, the enthusiasm of lines 15-44, the scorn and the praise of lines 45-60, the appeal, the prayer, the exultation of lines 61-68.

FOLLOW, OH FOLLOW! (58)

1. (*a*) See especially lines 101-134.
   (*b*) See her calm replies, lines 16, 39, 58, 148.
   (*c*) See lines 1-11, 22-23, 36-38. Remember his smile, line 41.
   (*d*) See lines 31-33.
   (*e*) See lines 155-159.

2. See question 1.
   Matilda's gay courage persuades us that she will meet ill fortune cheerfully. The friar's high spirits and love of song almost make us forget the overhanging clouds. The Baron's anger has its amusing side. We enjoy its fury, for we are never afraid of its consequences. The freedom and joy of the greenwood are near at hand.

   The style in which the passage is written makes for cheerfulness. Speeches are short, direct, lively. The opinions of daughter and father are sharply contrasted. Note the speed with which stroke follows stroke.

3. Matilda's cheerfulness under misfortune and her joy in the open air prepare us for her love of song.
   Her references to the swan (line 29) and to the eagle (line 59) are such as a poet might make.

   (*b*) The Baron's attitude towards what has befallen is that of the prudent father—a " prose " attitude. He has no sympathy with the high spirits of the friar. His comment upon Matilda's " lonely swan " is humorous and effective, but it is the comment of a " prose " mind.

4. The friar is ready to sing on any provocation. The faith " that will never be found again " (line 66) brings to his mind his song of the deer that is stolen away. As he sings he takes us straight to the greenwood. His high spirits and the Baron's outburst (lines 86-89) carry him naturally into his second song (line 93).

5. See preceding questions and notes.
   The difference between poetry and prose is not only, not even chiefly, one of rhyme and rhythm. (See " Hawke ", note 7, page 146).
   It is much more a difference of feeling. When we are " lifted " most completely out of ourselves, by some excitement of joy, or grief, or love, or hate, even—we come most near to poetry.
   Observe how the writer has led up to Matilda's song (line 63) in the rising excitement of the preceding dialogue (lines 44-61).

   By line 61 the contest with her father has carried Matilda above the level of ordinary prose. A girl of less spirit and less poetry might have relieved her feelings by " a good cry ", but for her, poetry is the natural " escape ". The friar has been discussed in note 4.
   (People like the Baron seldom soar above prose. When they are " uplifted ", they break forth into " strong language " (lines 86-89), or into violent action (lines 135-147). There is this to be said for the Baron, though, that, unlike most " strong language ", his has freshness and meaning.)

1. (*a*) John Huggins, like Cowper's John Gilpin, cut a poor figure on horse-back. The imp of mischief that lives in each of us likes to see " fish out of water ", people in undignified positions—holding hard to a runaway horse, it may be, or sitting in a furze-bush. Think of " The Priest and the Mulberry Tree " (page 32). In " Follow, Oh Follow ! " (page 58) the Baron is almost as ludicrous a " fish out of water " (lines 58-147).

   (*b*) Hood is one of our best punsters. A pun is that form of joke exemplified in line 2. It depends on the fact that words of the same sound may have altogether different meanings. " Shamble " means to shuffle along, but a shambles is a butcher's slaughterhouse. We rarely enjoy a joke that requires explanation, and, fortunately, you will see most of Hood's at once.

2. Choose for yourself. On jokes, as on poems, we must form our own opinions.

*   *   *

HUDIBRAS (67)

The Stewart line was restored to the British throne in 1660. " Hudibras ", a long satire on Puritans and Puritanism, was published in three parts, in 1663, 1664, 1668. Its theme made it popular at the time of its publication, and its style has maintained its fame through ages that have long ceased to hate the Puritans.

This extract comes from Part II, Canto 2.

1. Butler here accuses the Puritan colonists of twisting the law—not man's law, only, but God's law—to their own selfish purposes. He accuses the Puritans, generally, of smug hypocrisy, for he makes the Puritan who tells the story see nothing wrong in it, and speak of " this precious brother ", and " the saints ".

2. The theme—the hanging of one man for the crime of another—is not amusing in itself. The poet might have so treated it as to move us, not to laughter, but to anger and horror. But he wants us to laugh. He writes, therefore, in an easy, conversational style (see note 3). He does not wish us to think seriously of the weaver, and, accordingly, does not introduce him until the last line, when he is hanged before we can feel sorry for him. See, too, note 3 (*c*).

   We are to laugh at the absurdity of the Puritans' claims to righteous-ness, at their idea of " impartial justice " which so well suits their own convenience. By putting the story into the mouth of a Puritan, Butler

is able to cast more ridicule upon the sect. To ordinary people a murderer
is a murderer, but so smug are the " saints " that the cobbler is a " choice
malefactor ", a " precious brother " who slays an Indian in " mere zeal ".

Laughter can be more deadly than anger. Anger regards an enemy as
one's equal : laughter despises him.

3. (*a*) A prose version of the story would not have had the same pace. The
regular rhythm and the rapid rhymes carry us swiftly and smoothly to the
joke of the last line.

(*b*) Partly because of its pace, the verse brings a certain brightness into
the narrative. Compare lines 13-18 with this prose version :

> *The mighty Tottipottymoy sent an envoy to our elders, complaining
> sorely of Brother Patch's breach of the truce, and demanding that they
> either surrender the guilty person, or hang him themselves.*

The verse has a " snap " which the prose lacks.

(*c*) Lines 25-26. Note how the absurd rhyme—" stead did ", " bed-
rid "—makes the joke more farcical, still.

You will agree, too, that the irregular rhythm of

/   (/)   /   (/)   /
Hang an old weaver that was bed-rid

sounds less serious than a more regular line would have done.

/   /   /   /
Compare *Condemn a weaver that was bed-rid.*

*   *   *

MEDDLESOME MATTY (68)

This is a question that each reader must answer for himself or herself,
for there is no firmly-fixed fence between prose and poetry. What is
prose to one person may be poetry to another, while a third may find it
impossible to come to a decision.

We have found that writing which is prose in form may be really poetry
(note 5, page 165) and that writing in verse form may be merely doggerel
(note 7, page 146).

We shall all agree that this is a " teaching " story, and that it does not
lift us much, if at all, above the level of prose. Yet some of us may find
charm or delight in the telling of it. Ann Taylor writes tenderly. We
feel that she understands Matty (lines 19-44) and even sympathises with
her. Grandmamma, herself, was a little to blame (lines 13-16). And
Matty gives up the trick which hid her pleasantness. The language is
simple, well suited to the theme. The lines run very smoothly and
sweetly. The verse gives a lightness to the tale that could not have been
gained without it.

167

<u>MATILDA</u> (70)

1. " Meddlesome Matty " is a much more probable story than " Matilda ". A little girl might pry into a snuff-box, but a house is not likely to be burned down just because a girl told Dreadful Lies. The improbability is part of Mr. Belloc's fun.

2. The poem is a parody on the old-time " moral tale ". It amuses us by exaggerating all the absurdities into which the earlier writers fell.

   The capital letters of the first lines may supply a hint of the author's intention. Line 6, with its curious statement made still more odd by its odd rhyme " Matilda—killed her," prepares us to look for the humour which arrives with the Fire-Brigade.

3. Fable and poem have the same theme, that liars cannot expect to be believed. But " Matilda " is not designed to teach, but to amuse.

4. " And called the fire-brigade ". We may take " Immediate " and " Noble " for granted.

   Unnecessary adjectives are a source of weakness, not strength.

   Lines in similar style are 21, 22, 37, 44-6.

   The author is making fun of the stilted, would-be imposing style that was favoured by some of the writers he is imitating.

   In " Sandford and Merton " an " instructive " book published in 1789, a little boy reads aloud the story of " Androcles and the Lion " for the improvement of his friend, aged 6. Here is an extract :

   > *Presently a dreadful yell was heard, which struck the spectators with horror ; and a monstrous lion rushed out of a den, which was purposely set open ; and darted forward with erected mane, and flaming eyes, and jaws that gaped like an open sepulchre. A mournful silence instantly prevailed ! All eyes were directly turned upon the destined victim, whose destruction now appeared inevitable.*

   Lines 47, 48. The humour of those lines is heightened by their position immediately after the stilted lines 44-46. The crowd's words are the first words we should expect from an ordinary crowd, but the last we should expect from a crowd in a moral tale.

5. Capital letters were once used much more freely than they are to-day. Mr. Belloc may have wished to give an old-world air to his poem. Perhaps he had some moral tales in mind—for example, Æsop's Fables, where capital letters abound.

   Had Ann Taylor believed in capitals, she would have printed :

   > *One Ugly Trick has often Spoiled*
   > *The Sweetest and the Best.*

6. See preceding notes. Mr. Belloc has probably been amused by the strong belief of the moral tales that punishment always visits the wrongdoer, by the satisfaction they show in telling of its coming, by their pompous, grown-up style, their failure to look at anything with young eyes, their complete absence of humour.

168

We may feel that lifting the lid of the tea-pot is scarcely an ugly trick, and that, generally, the author is somewhat severe on Matty's meddlesomeness. We may wonder if the theme is one for a poem. We may dislike all poems with morals attached. But it is not likely we shall wish to parody Ann Taylor's actual writing. It is natural and simple, in no way pompous and absurd.

7. Very learned and very difficult books have been written on the subject of Laughter. We can, at least, say that we often laugh at absurd things in life and in books, at people in unusual circumstances, "fish out of water", at happenings that are quite contrary to custom or expectation. An important gentleman chasing his hat is more completely " out of water " than is a boy chasing his cap, and is, therefore, more laughable. The Baron and John Huggins are laughable because of the positions they find themselves in. Butler's story is laughable, partly because of the absurdity of hanging one man in place of another, partly because we are not accustomed to discuss death in so casual, so matter-of-fact a manner, partly because the Puritans, responsible for the death of the weaver, pride themselves on their righteousness. The story of Matilda is absurd and laughable because of the matter-of-fact way in which it is told—as if the burned child were of far less importance than the lesson which is learned from her. The writer has made us feel by his parody how false and unlifelike the moral tales could be.

* * *

THE SONG OF THE CYCLOPS (72)

"London's Tempe" was a show for Lord Mayor's Day, 29th October, 1629. It was arranged to celebrate the accession to office of Mr. James Campebell, " at the sole cost of the Right Worshipful Society of Ironmongers, his worthy fraternity ". This song is taken from the fourth scene, where Vulcan and the Cyclops, his servants, are working at the anvil. " Their habits are waist-coats and leather aprons, their hair black and shaggy, in knotted curls ".

1. No honest task is unworthy of a good workman. Vulcan and his servants would perform all useful work that the gods demanded. As lines 1, 2, 9-12 make us believe in the power of the Cyclops, so do lines 3 and 4 make us think of their neatness of hand. Lines 13-17 are more homely. It is amusing to think that Pan and the man in the moon required shoe-nails.

Dekker, no doubt, wished the citizens to realise the variety of tasks that fall to the lot of workers in iron.

2. Say the lines to yourself. " Thwick-a-thwack " is noisy and hard to say. It will accompany the swinging of the heavy hammers. " Pit-a-pat " is softer and comes more quickly off the tongue. The hammers here are lighter, are doing more delicate work, and are handled with greater ease.

169

3. (a) *We shoe the horses of the sun*

    Harness the dragons of the moon

    Forge Cupid's quiver, bow, and arrows

    And his dame's coach that's drawn with sparrows

  (b) *Till thwick-a-thwack, thwick ‖ thwack-a-thwack, thwack.*

4. Four boys may be the four smiths—Vulcan and the three Cyclops servants that Dekker gives him, Pyracmon, Brontes, Sceropes. Each boy may take a line of the stanza, and all will join in the chorus and in line 17.

    Read vigorously, but not too quickly, as though to a hammer accompaniment. Lay strong emphasis on the beats.

*   *   *

ELDORADO (73)

1. Is he the ghost of a former travetler? Is he Death? See lines 13, 14, 21. The poet does not tell us, and some of us may prefer to leave the question unanswered, even in our own minds.

2. The Mountains of the Moon was the name given by Ptolemy, one of the earliest geographers, to a mighty range of mountains that he thought must exist somewhere in Africa to feed the upper waters of the Nile. The poet uses the name here to indicate some mysterious barrier, unscaleable by man.

    The Twenty-Third Psalm speaks of the valley of the shadow of death.

    In the early days of the Spanish exploration of South America, tales of Eldorado, a land of wondrous wealth, lured many adventurers into the secret heart of the continent. No man has found it.

    We may think of Eldorado as that land of legend in South America, or we may think of it as that land of happiness that all men seek, at first in sunshine, " singing a song ", later with a shadow over their hearts, and to the end in vain.

3. We are told only that the knight was gallant and gaily bedight. (Note how few are the adjectives in those twenty-four lines) The poet is interested not in his seeker's appearance, nor in what he saw by the way, but in the idea of his unending and hopeless quest. It is a stern theme, and is best treated barely.

170

4. The addition of the stanza suggested would render the poem more common-place. Stanza 4 leaves with us a feeling of grim mystery. The fifth stanza would weaken this and put nothing new in its place. We know from the first that the knight was gallant. What Poe wishes us to feel at the end is that his quest was impossible.

Read the poem again, with some such fifth stanza as this:

> *Strength and hope gone,*
> *Struggled he on*
>   *Into the valley of the Shadow:*
> *And as his breath*
> *Faded in death,*
>   *He whispered, " Eldorado."*

The poem has become less powerful, less memorable.

5. The opening syllables are stressed in lines 1, 5, 10, 14, 16, 17, 19, 21, 22. In other lines—7, 9, 11, 13—we may open on a " beat ", if we care. Compare stanza 1 with this version:

> *In mail bedight*
> *A gallant knight*
>   *In sunshine and in shadow*
> *Had journeyed long,*
> *With mirth and song,*
>   *In search of Eldorado.*

Note how mechanical and stiff the new stanza is.

In lines 19, 21, 22, the stressed openings give weight and majesty to the shade's reply. For line 22 read " 'Tis fit you ride ", and note how much you lose.

See " The Lady of Shalott ", note B. 15 (page 191).

*   *   *

MY BONNIE MARY and THE FAREWELL (74)

1. The speaker is a Scotsman, setting out, it would appear, for the wars of the Continent. The wind blows down river, and everything is in trim for his departure. In lines 9-12 he pictures the fury of the battlefield.

2. Lines 1-12 are spoken by a Scotsman, a soldier who has been fighting in Ireland for James II against William III. His cause is lost, and he must now lead the life of an exile. Lines 19-30 are spoken by the soldier's wife or sweetheart, desolate in Scotland.

3. In almost every stanza line 4 is the most sad. With the repetition of it
in line 6, we feel the sadness still more keenly.

Lines 5 and 6 stay our pace, and force us to realise the eternity of the
parting.

Four-line stanzas would tell the story, but the six-line stanza makes us
feel that the lovers are actually present and speaking in our hearing. The
simplicity of line 5 is like a sob in the throat.

If meaning were all, then a prose version might be as powerful as the poem.
But we have found already that meaning is not all. See particularly
questions and notes on "September" (page 31) "Sea-weed" (page 48)
"Milk for the Cat" (page 53). See, too, "Lochinvar" (page 87) "Proud
Maisie" (page 119).

Note how bare is the language of "A Farewell", how many are the
words of one syllable, how few the appeals to our pity. Compare
"Winter" (page 47) "Eldorado" (page 73).

4. In "My Bonnie Mary" the excitement of the campaign is still to come,
and there is no suggestion that the parting is for ever. In "The
Farewell" courage and effort have been in vain. There is no hope of any
future meeting.

In the first poem only the man speaks. In the second we see what
failure means to the woman who must think and weep. Compare with
stanza 4 those lines written by the blind John Milton :

> *Thus with the year*
> *Seasons return, but not to me returns*
> *Day, or the sweet approach of even or morn,*
> *Or sight of vernal bloom, or Summer's rose,*
> *Or flocks, or herds, or human face divine ;*
> *But cloud in stead, and ever-during dark*
> *Surrounds me.*

*   *   *

JOHN O' LORN (76)

1. Both are brave. Burns's soldier accepts his fate with resignation and
strength. John o' Lorn gives fuller expression to his grief, but he has
fame and name and scars (line 7). No one but a brave man would have
the courage to say lines 7 and 8.

2. You must form your own opinion. We may think of Burns's soldier as
a Lowland Scot, one of a tight-lipped race, loath to put his deepest
feelings into words. John o' Lorn is more ready to lay his heart bare.
Not only has he a keen love of his green glens but a keen imagination that
tells him how his life will be spent in France—hungering for news of his
home, hungering for the touch of his own heather and bracken, for the
love of his friends.

172

3. Here you must choose for yourself.

4. When we read the first four lines, we understand the situation, and form an opinion of the speaker. After reading stanzas 2, 3, 4, we return to stanza 1 with the pleasure that comes from fuller knowledge. Conclude your reading of the poem at line 16, and you will feel that something is lacking. Only when you repeat the first stanza, in lines 17-20, do you have a sense of completeness. Compare " Up in the Morning Early " (page 51). The last line :

To the green glens, the fine glens we knew

said slowly, with due attention to the beats, gives weight and dignity to the whole poem.

※　　※　　※

CORONACH (77)

1. See lines 3-4, 17-19.

This poem comes from " The Lady of the Lake ", canto III. Roderick Dhu, a Highland chieftain, has called his clan to battle. The summons, a cross of yew, set on fire and quenched in blood, is being carried with all speed through his lands. Fisherman and huntsman, mower and smith, herdsman and ploughman leave their occupations and seize the weapons of war. But the message comes too late to Duncan of Duncraggan.

> *A gallant hunter's sport is o'er,*
> *A valiant warrior fights no more.*
> *Who, in the battle or the chase,*
> *At Roderick's side shall fill his place?*
> *Within the hall, where torches' ray*
> *Supplies the excluded beams of day,*
> *Lies Duncan on his lowly bier,*
> *And o'er him streams his widow's tear.*
> *His stripling son stands mournful by,*
> *His youngest weeps, but knows not why;*
> *The village maids and matrons round*
> *The dismal coronach resound.*

2. The mourners are Highland women whose thoughts turn naturally to the scenes amid which they live. Their comparison of the death of Duncan to the drying up of a fountain in summer is at once natural and beautiful. So are the contrasts drawn in stanza 2, and the similes of lines 21-24.

The Bible again and again makes us feel the beauty and the majesty of simple pictures drawn from nature and expressed in simple words. Think of Psalm 103 :

> *As for man, his days are as grass : as a flower of the field, so he flourisheth. For the wind passeth over it, and it is gone ; and the place thereof shall know it no more.*

173

3. In " Coronach " we " climb " from stanza to stanza. The third is the grandest, the most solemn. After line 24 any additional lines would seem weak.

4. All four poems are simple. They speak of things we can all understand, in words we can all follow. See note 2, above. The greatest things of life, joy and grief, love and death, are simple, and the most memorable writing upon those themes is simple. Compare " Annan Water " (page 38) and " Edom o' Gordon " (page 40) and note 3 (page 155).

5. In the four poems we have four different rhythms.

A great poet will turn a rhythm to his purpose. In " My Bonnie Mary " Burns uses a rhythm that other poets have used in humour. He produces the effect he wishes by the contrast of the thought in the last line of his stanza with that of the preceding lines.

In " The Farewell " the poet uses a rhythm that lends itself to the telling of an unadorned story of utter sorrow

Munro's John o' Lorn is quicker in mind, and has more to say than Burns's soldier. He speaks in longer lines, but note how the first and third lines of each stanza are pulled up by the second and the fourth.

Scott's mourners are women. In " Coronach " the rhythm and the double rhymes—" mountain ", " fountain ", etc.—give a softness, a tenderness to their lamenting.

There are rhythms, certainly, which do not seem appropriate to sad themes. We should not expect to find a lament written to the " tunes " of " The Fifteen Acres " (page 90) or " The Good News " (page 133).

*　　　*　　　*

THE FIGHTING TÉMÉRAIRE (78)

" Téméraire " means " bold ". The first ship of the name was in the navy of Louis XIV. The first British *Téméraire* was a 74-gun ship captured from the French at the battle of Lagos, in 1759, and sent out to join Rodney in the West Indies, in 1761. The vessel of our poem was a home-built 98-gun three-decker. She followed the *Victory* into the thickest of the battle at Trafalgar, where her great deeds gained her from the navy the proud name by which she is remembered. She was scrapped in 1838. One evening in that year Turner, the artist, was sailing on the Thames, when he saw the famous ship being towed to Deptford by "a little fiery, puny steam-tug ". The next year he exhibited his picture—now a national possession—" The Fighting Téméraire tugged to her last Berth ".

Sir Henry Newbolt has said that stanzas 5 and 6 of his poem refer to this picture.

1. Stanzas 1-4 refer to Trafalgar day, the great day in the history of the ship. The hostile fleets were in sight of each other when dawn broke on 21st October 1805, but the wind was so light that the first shots were not fired until noon, and it was sometime later when the *Téméraire* went into action.

For stanzas 5 and 6, see the note, page 174. Turner's picture shows the ship under an evening sky.

We may like to think that morning, noon, and evening represent the three stages in the life of the ship, the times of preparation, of triumph, of "great days done". A writer has said that Turner's object in his picture was to give the *Téméraire* a ghostly, unearthly look, as if already more a melancholy vision of the past than any present reality.

2. In stanzas 1, 3, 5, the poet speaks, as it were, in his own person, but in the italicised stanzas he sets before us the imagined singing of the gunner's lads and the phantom voice.

3. (a) In each stanza the rhymes are arranged thus : *a b a b a a a b*. All the "*a*" rhymes are double. Note the resemblance between this scheme and the *a b a b c c c b* of "Hawke" (page 21).

(b) Stanzas 1, 3, 5 rhyme throughout on the same two sounds. In stanzas 2, 4, 6 the "*a*" rhymes are not repeated from stanza to stanza.

(c) By beginning stanzas 1, 3, 5, each with a "ringing" line, and by rhyming on two sounds throughout, the poet directs attention to the fact that he has drawn three "companion" pictures of the *Téméraire*. (See note 1). And because the pictures have been drawn all in one style, the contrast between the first two and the third is made all the clearer. The poet does not ask us to note the contrast or to feel its pathos. The recurring rhymes force it upon us.

Note one change in the rhythm of stanza 5. Lines 4 and 8, 20 and 24 run easily, almost speedily. But listen to lines 36 and 40 :

Of the great days done

To the great days done.

The very sound tells us that all is over, that a chapter is ended.

4. "Hawke" is a poem of pride and triumph ; "The Fighting Téméraire" a poem of pride and regret—regret that a great ship, powerful and beautiful and famous, must "fade down the river".

If you have seen a copy of Turner's picture, you will understand the mood in which Sir Henry Newbolt wrote this poem.

SPRING, THE SWEET SPRING (80)

1. The first two are the cuckoo and the nightingale. Is the third the lapwing or one of the finches ; the fourth the owl or the wood-pigeon ? Which birds would you rather include in a Spring choir? Which tune the merrier lays to you ?

2. The rhyme-scheme is *a a a a a a b*. Stanza 2 is rhymed in similar fashion. Stanza 3 is rhymed *a a a a a a b c*.

    Those six rhymes on the one sound help to bring out the poet's simple delight in the season, to make us feel that we are actually listening to birds singing. See " The Hunt is Up " (page 19 ; notes, page 145).

    With stanza 1 compare this version :

    > *Spring, the sweet time, is the year's pleasant king ;*
    > *Then blooms each flower, then maids dance in a ring,*
    > *Cold doth not bite, the pretty birds do sing,*
    > *Cuckoo, jug-jug, pu-we, to-witta-woo.*

3. The season suggests a host of happy thoughts to him, and he sets them down, without taking time to pause, one after the other, as they come to him. As we read, we, too, feel that Spring is overflowing with happiness. Compare " Lines Written in March " (page 83).

4. Here is a possible stanza :

    > *The golfer tees, the stumps are set in threes,*
    > *Yachts sail the seas, cars scurry thick as bees,*
    > *From sky and trees are borne upon the breeze,*
    > *Cuckoo, jug-jug, pu-we, to-witta-woo.*

5. See notes 2 and 3. The short half-lines, with their strong, clear rhymes have the cheerfulness and the rhythm of bird-song.

6. It is his last exclamation of delight, as though he had tried to sum all up in a cry of joy. Remember all you have said in lines 1-12, and bring this out in your reading.

*　　　*　　　*

THE MERRY BEGGARS (81)

1. Make your own choice, but see " The Wraggle Taggle Gipsies " (page 24) " Johnnie Faa " (page 26) " Follow, Oh Follow ! " (page 60). The first, especially, counts house and possessions poor things beside the freedom of the open field.

2. Line 9. Note how the change in the rhythm enlivens it. Compare it with the regular

    > " *Cuckoo*," *cries he* ; " *Jug, jug*," *sings she.*

3. Nash sings like a bird ; his poem is one call of joy. He does not argue with us ; he has no time for that. He simply says, " Look and listen," and we do look and listen.

    In his second stanza Brome seems almost to deride men because they let other things interfere with the joy of the season. And as he has thought of those other things, so do we.

1. The prose mentions the hamlet, and describes in careful detail the colours of the trees. It gives a fuller account of the pasture and the work in the field.

2. The poem mentions the whooping plough-boy in place of the barking dog, and gives a clearer picture of the sky.

3. The prose writer notes all that she sees. The poet has his eye on the landscape before him, the lake, the fields, the hill, the sky. Detailed references to the trees would crowd his picture, and take away something of its simplicity. See, too, note 7, below.

4. Though Wordsworth paints a mountain prospect, and Clare more domestic scenes, both are interested particularly in cheerful movement and cheerful sounds, rather than in the colours before them. Note how sparing they are in their use of adjectives of colour.

5. Line 5 alone is entirely without movement. Note how the repeated vowel sound in " green field sleeps " comes soothingly to the ear. The short " two-beat " lines move quickly, piling up one on another. The four long lines, 5, 10, 15, 20, all retard our pace. Note that the cattle, too, are almost motionless ; the plough-boy, instead of hastening, cries " Anon-anon " ; the rain has stopped.

6. Both are good. The crowing cock strikes the key-note of the poem. In line 1 the poet prepares us for " the joy " and " the life " (lines 16, 17) that he wishes us to share with him. The last line sums up. The storm of the previous day (see prose, line 1) is a thing of the past. Nothing remains to mar our pleasure.

7. The poet does not tell us in so many words that he is delighted. It is his aim rather to make us feel with him the happiness of this day that has brought the Spring. He has chosen every detail to convey this happiness (notes 3, 4, 6). It is important for him that young and old alike are at work in the field, rather than that they are ploughing, harrowing, and sowing (prose, line 20) that the cattle are feeding " as one ", rather than that their exact number is forty-two. He thinks of the snow as a beaten enemy, and of the hills and the springs as rejoicing in its defeat.

   The poem moves at a brisk pace. Cheerful statements are made in quick succession. The lines are short. Rhymes come close together. Compare " The Hunt is Up " (page 19) " September " (page 31) " Spring, the Sweet Spring " (page 80).

1. See line 20. The line suggests a warmer country than England, where Spring is richer in colour, but not so fresh and bright. Actually, Browning was in Italy.

2. (*a*) Three pictures are suggested in the poem—the elm-tree (lines 3-7) the thrush in the pear-tree (lines 11-16) the fields (lines 17-19).

(*b*) Each is a morning picture (see lines 13 and 17). The poem breathes the air of dewy mornings, before the sun is high, when the birds are most lavish of their song.

3. (*a*) The second picture is painted most fully. The pear-tree " leans " to the field, and at the end of a branch, so slender that it bends with his weight, sits the singing thrush. But each picture is clear and true. All who know the country in Spring will feel the truth of such words as " unaware ", " careless rapture ", " rough ".

(*b*) See lines 14-16. The song of the thrush is the fullest and richest of all our bird songs, though it is so short :

The first fine careless rapture.

When we hear a beautiful melody, or a beautiful line of poetry, we wish to hear it again, and in its repetition we find an added pleasure.

4. The fresh dewy mornings, the joyous bird song, the greenness of the English Spring, the wealth of blossom in May.

5. Most poems of longing are sad. But this poet remembers England in Spring-time so vividly that in imagination he is able to return to it and be happy. Only in the last line, with a shock, does he " come to earth " in Italy.

6. (*a*) See " The Witches' Charm " (page 50) and note 3 (*b*) (page 160).

(*b*) Decide for yourself. But note how well the irregular form accords with the excitement of the poet, passing in rapture from one beloved scene to another " in England—now ! "

*   *   *

DIVINATION BY A DAFFODIL and OF BEAUTY (85)

1. There is no contradiction ; let us say, rather, that the poets look at the season from different points of view. Spring is still gay and beautiful, though flowers, and men, too, must wither. Indeed, it is only because he loves the Spring so intensely, that the sight of the daffodil makes Herrick feel how quickly it fleets away. Compare his " To Daffodils " (page 93).

2. We may call them serious, but if we find beauty in them we shall not call them sad.

"The Farewell" and "Coronach" tell of sorrows which have befallen particular men and women, personal sorrows which are much harder to bear than a general regret that youth has passed so quickly, with all its freshness and joy. But neither are those poems wholly sad, if they are beautiful to us.

*   *   *

JOCK O' HAZLEDEAN (86)

1. Errington and Langley-dale have an English sound, but Jock's name is Scots, and line 31 makes it clear that the lady lived south of the Border.

2. Frank's father may be the speaker.

3. Most probably it is the lady's mother who reproves her and points out how good a "match" has been arranged for her. Note the change of tone—the commands in lines 9 and 10, the use of the word "wilfu'".

4. (a) Lines 21, 22 point fairly clearly to Frank as the speaker.

   (b) The bribes are not unlike those with which the lord tried to lure the lady back from the Wraggle Taggle Gipsies (page 24). They are not so dull, certainly.

5. (a) This poem is written in an eight-line stanza, while most ballads are in fours, but it preserves the four-beat and three-beat metre. It opens abruptly, makes abrupt changes from one speaker to another, and leaves the reader to supply details.

   (b) You have been told (note 4, page 154) that the ballad tells a story and tells it barely. Note how much more bare is stanza 1 than are Scott's imitations of it. With stanza 2 we seem to enter another world, almost; a world much closer to the one we know.

6. In most respects Scott has kept to the form of the original. He has retained the rhythm and the stanza pattern, though he has given additional rhymes (lines 1 and 3, 5 and 7 in each stanza). More important, he has not repeated his fourth line in his fifth, as the old poem does, and he loses thereby something of the old-world charm. Note how happily he has turned lines 7 and 8 into a refrain in stanzas 2 and 3, and how triumphantly he breaks away from the refrain in lines 31 and 32.

179

<u>LOCHINVAR</u> (87)

1. The poems are alike in theme. An English lady in love with a Scotsman, is tempted to marry another suitor, and at the last moment escapes " o'er the Border and awa' ".

   In " Jock o' Hazledean " we are told principally of the temptations, and the hero of the story does not appear.

   " Lochinvar " tells of the escape, an escape more dashing and spectacular than the flight of the ladie who " loot the tears down fa' ".

2. The father has spirit. He is hot-tempered, doubtless, and obstinate, the typical " stern parent ", but we feel he is a fit opponent to Lochinvar.

   The mother, too, has spirit, though she is perhaps less choleric than her husband. She frets while he fumes.

   The poet has described the bridegroom in lines 11, 16, 34. We feel he was certainly not first in the pursuit (lines 43-45).

3. The prose, in a plain way, begins at the beginning of the story. As plain prose should, it explains why Lochinvar was prompted to come out of the West that day. But all the excitement, all the adventure, have gone out of it. It tells us nothing of the hero's impetuous gallop to Netherby, and keeps from us much of the sheer audacity of his reply to Ellen's father. We cannot, therefore, sympathise with him as we should do. The poem opens, ballad-like, in the middle of the story. We are on horseback from the first, travelling by the hero's side and, thanks to the metre, we gallop to the last line.

4. Line 46 : *But the lost bride of Netherby ne'er did they see.*

5. It will not be easy to capture in ballad metre all the high spirits of the original. The specimen stanza (page 89) is not unlike stanza 2 of " Annan Water " (page 38) a poem in a different key.

6. " Lochinvar " is a horseman's story, and the metre gallops as it should. Compare " How They Brought the Good News from Ghent to Aix " (page 133) and " The Cavalier's Escape " (page 136). Even when the hero has dismounted, the long swinging lines convey admirably his dashing courage and the speed of his actions.

*   *   *

<u>THE FIFTEEN ACRES</u> (90)

1. The Fifteen Acres is probably the name of the field where the little wee nest is built.

2. The gusty poop may be the wind-rocked topmost branch of a tree. The azure flooring is the sky, the floor of Heaven.

3. The poet has written each stanza as one sentence.

180

4. There are twelve in stanza 1 ; fourteen in stanza 2 ; thirteen in stanza 3.

5. Stanza 1 : cling. swing, sing, fling, wing, bring, swing, sing, sing, sing (10).

   Stanza 2 : flit, twit, bit, sit, fit, knit, mill, hill (8).

   Stanza 3 : skim, swim, rim, drip, slip, slip, slip (7).

6. Eight. Seventy-seven words, nine in every ten, are one-syllabled.

7. He has planned to turn into words the tireless, clear, simple joy of the bird's song. You have, no doubt, discovered this from your reading, but your study of the poem must have given you an insight into his skill that you would not otherwise have had. Joy unending overflows in the long swift-running sentences. In the quick succession of the rhymes we hear the ever-repeated phrases of the song. The " i " rhymes convey its clear, high notes, the great number of short words its bright simplicity.

   It is not at all likely that the poet said to himself, " I must write in long sentences and short lines, with many rhymes and a high proportion of one-syllabled words." Rather, he had listened to the song till the joy of it was in his heart, and, because he was a poet, the words and lines and rhymes came to him. One feels that this poem, or most of it, was written with speed, " at a white heat."

8. The " oo " rhymes let us hear the wind.

9. At the end of each flight the bird returns to its nest and its mate, the source of its wild delight.

10. Read it with all the " fine careless rapture " of which you are capable.

*   *   *

MAGDALEN (92)

Mary Magdalen was a disciple of Christ, one of " certain women which had been healed of evil spirits and infirmities " and " ministered unto him of their substance " (Luke, viii, 2 and 3). She was among the women who witnessed the crucifixion, " beholding afar off " (Matthew, xxvii, 55). She sat " over against the sepulchre " in which Joseph of Arimathæa laid the body of Jesus (Matthew, xxvii, 61), and was the first to whom Jesus appeared after He had risen from the grave (Mark, xvi, 9).

1. Because he was a poet. The lesson is plain for all to read. Any pointing of it would be hurtful to the grave beauty of the poem.

181

TO DAFFODILS (93)

1. Line 2 : The hanging head of the flower may have reminded him with particular force of the quick decay of all beautiful things. But Herrick has many poems on the same theme—" To Blossoms ", " To Meadows ", " Gather ye rosebuds while ye may ", " To Violets ". The hanging heads may have suggested also the beautiful ninth line of " To Daffodils ".

2. (a) The rhyme-scheme for each stanza is *a b c b d d c e a e*. You will note how cunningly the lines are woven together, how lines 1 and 3, which seem at first unrhymed, are linked up with lines 9 and 7.

(b) Read the poem as a regular eight-line stanza—lines 1-4, followed by :

> *Stay, stay until the hasting day*
> *Has run to even-song*

followed by lines 9-10.

Where the short lines asked us to pause and reflect, this version runs along briskly and " ordinarily ". We have lost the delicate, swaying beauty of the rhythm, as of flowers on a spring morning.

3. (a) Lines 21-24. The comparison of man's life in its brevity to water-drops that glisten and are gone has appealed to writers at all times. Compare Job, vii, 9 : *As the cloud is consumed and vanisheth away : so he that goeth down to the grave shall come up no more.*

(b) Both passages are beautiful. Scott's poem laments the death of a Highland chieftain, and the comparisons in it are drawn from mountain scenery. They are piled one on another as though to stress the suddenness of Duncan's death. Herrick's lines apply to all men. (See note 2, page 179). The actual words are simple—only four in stanza 2 are of more than one syllable—and they say nothing that has not been said since the world was young. But they flow as smoothly as water. Not a phrase has been turned from its natural shape to meet the demands of metre or rhyme. Not a word could be changed without loss.

*   *   *

DAFFODILS (94)

1. The bright waters of a lake lay before him. Trees grew on its bank, their branches bare as yet of leaves. (See " A Spring Scene ", page 82, line 11.) Under them stretched a never-ending line of golden daffodils. It was a windy and a sunny day, typical of April. The flowers fluttered and danced in the breeze, and shone golden in the sunlight. The waves sparkled.

2. Not only were they continuous as the stars, but, like them, they shone and twinkled—a line of dancing light.

182

3. They tossed their heads in sprightly dance and outdid the waves in glee. But not merely did they *seem* jocund to the poet as they did to his sister ("A Busy Highway", lines 11, 12). Wordsworth believed that flowers were actually happy. Compare this stanza from "Lines Written in Early Spring":

> *Through primrose tufts, in that green bower,*
> *The periwinkle trailed its wreaths;*
> *And 'tis my faith that every flower*
> *Enjoys the air it breathes.*

He is *in* the *company* of the daffodils (line 16) sharing their joy.

4. He was lonely in stanza 1, not sad, not even solitary—his sister was with him (page 95)—but away from the world, "lonely as a cloud that floats on high", wrapt in thought, "pensive". When the golden host flashed upon his sight he was at once in their company, and gay because of their joy.

5. (*a*) "Flash" and "dance".

(*b*) "All at once" he saw the flowers (line 3). Like the stars, they "shone" and "twinkled" (lines 7, 8). They "outdid the *sparkling* waves in glee" (line 14).
"Dance" is repeated in each stanza (lines 6, 12, 13, 24).
The daffodils were golden and glad, tossing their heads in joy.
Here is another stanza from "Lines Written in Early Spring":

> *The budding twigs spread out their fan,*
> *To catch the breezy air;*
> *And I must think, do all I can,*
> *That there was pleasure there.*

6. See stanza 4. The picture of the dancing daffodils came before his mind's eye, ever and again, whether he were idly dreaming or deep in thought. He had delighted so much in the show that it was his for all time, a wealth of happiness, "a joy for ever".

A BUSY HIGHWAY (95)

1. It is clear that the poet and his sister are writing of the same scene, the lake-side ablaze with daffodils. The prose gives us details the poem omits. It mentions the "advance-guard" of the host, the width of the long belt, the little knots and stragglers apart from the main body, the mossy stones and the flowers that rested upon them. It tells us at the close that the waters were stormy, with waves that sounded like the sea. The poet's attention is held by the shining, dancing host beside the dancing waves. See the notes which follow.

2. No. It was the great host of flowers that "all at once" caught his attention, lured him from his thoughts, made him one of the jocund company.

3. The poet's aim is not to "photograph" the scene, but to share with us the pleasure he had in it. See "Lines Written in March" (page 83) and

note 7 (page 177). The reference to the turnpike road enables us to estimate exactly the breadth of the " belt ", but it does not suggest the multitude of flowers, that was part of his pleasure, as do the words he uses—" a crowd ", " a host ", " a never-ending line ".

Compare with lines 7-10 of the poem the following :

> *Broad as a country turnpike road,*
> *That takes the traveller on his way,*
> *They stretched, continuous, where flowed*
> *The shallow waters of a bay.*

The road is much too hum-drum to find a place in the poem. It is introduced above to convey an idea of breadth, but it brings with it ideas of solidity and flatness that we cannot associate with the dancing daffodils. The stars of the Milky Way, to which the poet compares them, are not only continuous, a " highway " across the heavens, but a shining highway.

4. The picture of the weary flowers is a beautiful one, but there was no place for it in a poem of glad movement. It was the dancing flowers that Wordsworth saw. Herrick might have seen the others. (See pages 85, 93.)

5. Lines 11-14. Here Dorothy Wordsworth does not merely record facts, but shows us what the scene has meant to her. Only in form are those lines different from poetry. See " Follow, Oh Follow ! " (page 58) and note 5 (page 165). The writer is carried by her joy in the scene to a level above that of ordinary prose.

6. (*a*) See notes 1, 3, 4, 5. The prose gives a fuller account of the scene. Tne poet has selected only the details that were of importance to him—the details that composed the picture of joy.

(*b*) See notes 3 and 6. Dorothy Wordsworth tells us that " the daffodils *seemed* as if they verily laughed with the wind." We can understand this ; their tossing, dancing movements gave an impression of gaiety. But in the poem they *were* a jocund company. The flowers and the waves were glad together, and the poet's heart danced *with* them.

*   *   *

GIPSY SONG and THE BELLMAN (96)

1. Any night journey is exciting, but the song suggests adventure and romance. We are to travel in the light of stars and moon, and under the mysterious faery beam. The hint of danger from the fire-drake lures us on. Will the spell prevail ? There is excitement, too, in the rhythm. The short, quick-rhyming lines urge us to be gone.

   Contrast the friendly excitement of this poem with the sinister excitement of " The Witches' Charm " (page 50).

2. The lines come softly to us, comforting as a friendly charm, expressive of good-will. The last couplet tells us that the dread hours are past, the evils of the night are vanquished, and the cheerful day is at hand.

184

1. He must have known it. He has chosen its theme, has treated it in the same manner, and employed the same stanza form. Herrick was a friend of Jonson and an admirer of his work. One poet's success in discovering a new stanza often inspires another to put it to a different use.

2. The pictures differ in detail. Jonson's night is lit by a full moon, Herrick's only by the stars, and so, most beautifully, he calls to Julia's aid the glow-worm and the elves.

3. Herrick's night is the more friendly. Jonson's night has a moon, but her light is almost uncanny, and the fire-drake may be abroad. There is no ghost in Herrick's, and the elves with their glowing eyes will be guardians against Will o' th' Wisp and snake. Herrick's stars do not glister, but give a calm light " like tapers clear without number ".

4. Jonson's demands a quicker, " wilder " reading. His gipsies have no time for main verbs in the statement of their first wishes, and the boy with the bow is to run. Julia is to walk lightly " on, on her way ".
Many of Herrick's lines will suffer from a hasty reading.
Study these from stanza I :

> *Her eyes the glow-worm lend thee*
> *And the elves also*
> *Whose little eyes glow.*

Only one of Jonson's must be taken slowly :

> *Till the fire-drake hath o'ergone you.*

5. Here you must choose for yourself.

*   *   *

PUCK (98)

1. Puck is a spirit of mischief, but not of evil, a practical joker, a merry wanderer of the night. He tells us that he is Oberon's jester, but we feel his tricks are played in the first place for his own amusement. Plainly, he enjoys spilling the ale, and tumbling the wisest aunt. He is not malicious. None of his jests causes grievous harm, and he can be friendly to those who speak well of him.

2. The Fairy seems a little doubtful of Puck. She has seen him before, and has heard of his escapades, but his tricks are not amusing to her. She speaks of the *breathless* housewife and of the night-wanderers' *harm*. We feel that she and he go different ways. She is of the woods and secret places, a member of Titania's train (page 102). We cannot think of Puck away for long from the villages and farms.

In a play a writer cannot pause to describe a character directly. Note how Shakespeare has painted Puck's portrait by means of question and reply.

3. (a) Read the Fairy's speech more slowly and quietly, perhaps with little doubtful pauses.

(b) Puck is thoroughly well pleased with himself. He recounts his deeds with obvious delight and pride. Take his speech at a quick, confident speed.

* * *

THE MAD AND MERRY PRANKS OF ROBIN GOOD-FELLOW (99)

1. Most of Robin's pranks are referred to in the passage from " A Midsummer Night's Dream " (page 98). In this longer poem some are described in greater detail.

Compare	PUCK	ROBIN GOOD-FELLOW
	line 8	stanza 3
	lines 8, 13-15	stanza 4
	lines 4, 16-26	stanza 5
	lines 9-10	stanza 6

Lines 11-14 of " Robin Good-fellow " have no counterpart in the previous poem, but Puck says elsewhere in the play :

> *I'll put a girdle round about the earth*
> *In forty minutes.*

Robin's hatred of ghosts is not openly shared by Puck, though we learn from the play that he and Oberon are " spirits of another sort ".

2. Both are mad and merry, delighting in their pranks and exulting in the confusion that they cause. They are spirits of good-humour, in no way the enemies of mortals, and ready to surprise them at times by acts of service as well as of mischief. To take a man or woman out of the humdrum rut, to provide a merry hour, to spice life with unexpected and usually ridiculous happenings—this is their calling and their sport.

Robin may seem the more uncanny, though it is hard to say why. Perhaps line 2 creates an eerie atmosphere. His rhythm is jerkier, more " sudden ", more exciting than Puck's.

3. In each stanza lines 5 and 6, and lines 8 and 9 might have been written as single lines with mid-rhyme.

Perhaps the poet felt that the short lines conveyed something of Robin's swiftness and abruptness of movement. Like him they " start and snort " (line 46).

* * *

FAIRY LULLABY (102)

1. Yes, if we do not feel that the phrase is too clumsy to apply to those "quaint spirits ". Their coats are made from bats' wings. Their enemies are thorny hedgehogs, spiders (long legged spinners) beetles. Even their speech is " small ", like that of little children : *You spotted snakes with double tongue. Weaving spiders, come not here.*

186

2. The Fairies and Puck have little in common. They are gentle spirits, loving the beauty of the flowers, and the melody of the nightingale, hating the clamorous owl. Puck, here, is a rough-and-tumble goblin, an imp of mischief, sprung from the imaginations of the " villagery ".

3. It is calm and beautiful. Note how gently the Fairies charm away the woodland enemies—" Be not seen." " Do no wrong." " Come not near." Violent words are foreign to their nature. Hear how the " l " sound runs through the chorus like the notes of the nightingale.

*　　*　　*

ARIEL'S SONG (104)

He loves the same delicately beautiful things. But his is a song of escape, not of service, a song of freedom to fly after summer merrily, to suck where the bee sucks, to couch in the cowslip and under the swinging blossom.

*　　*　　*

FAREWELL, REWARDS AND FAIRIES (105)

1. (a) The fairies.
(a) Countryfolks who lived in the " fairy " age.
(c) Queen of England, 1553-1558. She restored Roman Catholicism, which had been abandoned by her father, Henry VIII, and her brother, Edward VI.

2. See lines 17-24. Bishop Corbet suggests that they vanished when England gave up Catholicism. " Dymchurch Flit ", one of the tales in Kipling's " Puck of Pook's Hill ", tells of their going.—" Fair or foul, we must flit out o' this, for Merry England's done with, an' we're reckoned among the Images ". The Puritans, certainly, denounced belief in them as wicked. But the fairies always seem to have flourished a short time ago, in the days of people's great-grandfathers. The poet Chaucer (1340-1400) makes one of his characters declare that they had been driven from England by the friars.

3. To Puck. Those pretty ladies are not so " quaint " as Titania. The poet tells us they rewarded their favourites, as Puck did, and lived, like him, in close touch with humankind

4. See line 15. The poet has added an additional " merrily ", so that we may feel that the old-time dances went with a swing.

5. Corbet was a jovial bishop, a lover of good-fellowship and happiness. The Puritans to him were glum spoil-sports who had destroyed the Merry England that had been, the England in which Puck had played his pranks. His poem is a lament for the good old cheerful days. Did he believe in fairies ? He believed, at least, in what the fairies stood for. He thought that to attack the fairies was narrow-minded folly. And if, with half of his mind, as it were, he felt that once they had danced upon the heath, he was no worse a bishop, and no worse a poet.

187

1. They are gods and planets, both—shining gods, eloping planets. Venus is luminous and supple. Mars is a comely warrior on earth and his place in heaven is empty.   The poem has all the happy inconsequence of a dream.

2. See lines 28-33. Mortal men give (and ask) reasons, but women are sometimes allowed to act without them. And Venus is a goddess. Was it the stars in his eyes that moved her, or pity for him, or her sense of fun? Lines 30-32 are only to influence Mars. Perhaps gods are more " practical " than goddesses.

3. Tuesday, to the Romans, was Mars's day and Friday was Venus's day. The French names for them are Mardi and Vendredi.

4. " Disaster " (from Greek, *dis* and *astron*, a star) is something that happens under an unlucky star. Now this " disaster " is himself a star.

5. Like Venus, he does not answer our question, but he was interested in him, perhaps amused by him, probably a little sorry for him, too. Forgotten are his scrapings and capers, and, though only twice a week, he shines in the heavens.

6. (*a*) The lines take a new meaning when we return to them. " Once upon a time " (line 43) reminds us of all that has befallen. We look down as it were, on the old days, from " somewhere between Venus and Mars ". They are good lines to read, and we are glad to have the opportunity of saying them twice over.

(*b*) The repetition in lines 44 and 45 emphasises the difference between what was and what is. In your reading you may take lines 42 and 43 as you took lines 1 and 2, and bring out the change by a proud stress on " Once " in line 44.
" Sublime " (line 48) is a triumphant ending.

7. It is unusual in theme, in treatment, in rhythm. Surely this is the only dancing-master who ever encountered Venus and Mars! The treatment of the deities is fresh. Venus is like a girl on a holiday.

The metre, too, breaks away from the every-day. The lines vary in length, as they may well do in so " irregular " a story, but the poem speeds smoothly on its way. Read it with the minimum of stresses.

Soon they were far from earth and high in heaven,

Those Lovers serene,

And on a Tuesday or a Friday even

You may see the star that dances in between.

THE LADY OF SHALOTT (108)

A

1. The contents of each part may be suggested by the following: I, Shalott. II, Shadow-life. III, Lancelot. IV, The Curse. Note how one part leads into, and explains, that which follows.

2. It is a broad, slow-flowing stream, with barges moving upon its waters. Willows clothe its banks, and behind them fields of barley and rye rise gradually to the uplands. Some distance above the river and following its course passes the highway along which travels a varied throng of the folks of the Middle Ages (lines 55-61).

3. It is a secret and silent island, shut off by willow and aspen trees from the eyes of travellers by the river, and having no speech with them. Water-lilies grow by its banks. A grey castle rises in its midst, a still place, remote from the life of road and river.

4. She is a solitary and mysterious lady, a fairy lady to the reapers. We are told only that her face was lovely (line 169). She has heard but a whisper of the curse upon her. She is happy weaving the gay shadows of real life that the mirror presents to her, or nearly happy (lines 64-72). A fuller description would take away something of her mystery. Compare " La Belle Dame sans Merci ", notes 3 and 6 (page 193) and " Count Arnaldos ", note 4 (page 194).

5. We are left to fill in much of the colour for ourselves. The poet has given us the red of the girls' cloaks, the crimson of the page. From his suggestions we can make our web gay as we please. The troops of damsels, the knights, the pageantry of the funeral will have for contrast the duller tones of the village-churls. For background we have the greens and yellows of trees and fields. Actual colours are used sparingly. Lancelot must stand out clear in shining armour, and he is all the brighter because the ordinary figures have not been painted in detail.

6. The shadow-sight of the happy lovers (line 70) has made the lady long for reality. Lancelot is the very embodiment of life. He " flashes " into the mirror like a meteor. Picture the scene—the blue sky, the yellow grain, the glitter of armour, of shield, of bridle, of bugle, of saddle, of helmet and feather, " one burning flame ". The knight's brow glows in the sunlight, and the hooves of his horse are burnished. Bridle bells and armour ring out in the unclouded, sunlit air, and his own joyous song speaks of strength and joy.

7. We have passed in an instant from dazzling sunshine to weeping skies, from shining life to death. Compare " La Belle Dame sans Merci " (lines 33-36).

8. It seems fitting that Lancelot, who all unwittingly has caused the curse to fall upon the Lady, should praise her beauty and offer a prayer for her soul.

This is a " fairy " story, but in real life, too, men may be ignorant of matters that concern them very nearly. Like Lancelot, they may be pawns in a game played by fate.

189

B

1. The fields are *long*, for they stretch from the river's edge to the sky-line. They *clothe* the wold—rising ground that would be bare without the crops of barley and rye. The people on the road go *up and down*, for the country slopes towards Camelot, the *many-towered*, the royal city whose spires are prominent in the distant view. They do not merely look, but *gaze*, as though trying to probe the secret of the island that lies *below* them in a stretch of the river so quiet that lilies grow in its waters.

2. *Whiten* : The breezes reveal the silvery undersides of the willow leaves. Compare " A Song " (page 45).
Quiver : The leaves of the aspen tremble in the slightest wind.
Dusk : The quiet water is ruffled and darkened by the breezes.
Shiver : Tiny ripples are formed.
Dim : It is night-time ; the river is broad ; the sky is heavy with rain.
Bold : The Lady, like the seer, has dared to look into her own future.
Glassy : She is in a trance. Her face is grey and without expression.

3. See note A, 6. " Dazzling " " flamed " " sparkled " " glitter'd " " shone " " burn'd " " glow'd " " burnish'd ". Note the number of " flashing " words and the care with which each is used. Note, too, the comparison of the bridle to a branch of stars, and of the knight's sudden and shining passage to a meteor, trailing light. " Flashed " conveys two ideas—the brilliance of the image in the mirror, and the suddenness of its appearance.

4. The autumn wind blows more freely on the uplands than in the still valley of the river. The air is fresher and lighter.
Two pictures of Lancelot flash into the mirror, the one of himself upon the road, the other of his reflection in the water.

5. See lines 136-137, 140. The loosely-flowing white robes suggest the swan's plumage, and the word " floats " the swan's motion.

6. The " is " sound is thin and quiet. The whole line whispers, like the reaper, half eager, half afraid.

7. The word conveys a good picture of the villagers, least joyful by far of all the wayfarers. The gruff " ur " sound is repeated in " churls ".

8. The line contains four " r " sounds. " Rung ", itself, is full of sound.

9. There are three " st " sounds. The line " strains ". You cannot say it quickly.

10. The solemn " o " of " mournful " " holy " " lowly " " frozen " " slowly " " wholly ".

11. See line 21. Lines 19-21 " trail " with the horses. Try to say them quickly. The unexpected pause in mid-line emphasises the sluggish movement. Lines 22-23, on the other hand, invite us to hasten.

12. All the actions mentioned lead up to the last fatal one which brings the curse. The repetition of " She " increases our excitement at each action. The substitution of " and " makes the whole passage common-place. The lines are abrupt and jerky, to convey something of the quick, tense movements of the Lady.

190

13. See note **11.** There are two slight mid-line pauses here, in lines 67, 68. Note the three " u " sounds, and note how you destroy the beauty of "with plumes and lights and music " if you say the words quickly.

14. See notes A, 6, and B, 3. There was no hint of Lancelot's coming, he " flashed " into the mirror.

15. The poet gives variety and beauty to his rhythm by using both stressed and unstressed openings. Compare " Eldorado " and note 5 to that poem (pages 73 and 171). Lines 28-36 open on stressed syllables. Line 36 is " Lady of Shalott ", not " The Lady of Shalott ". Note, too, that the rhymes are double. The stanza is quiet and gently-moving, suggestive of the hush of early morning and late evening. Lines 55-63 are lively, telling of the succession of travellers. They invite us to read them at a brisk pace, with little or no stress on the opening syllables—all but line 63, where the emphasis on " She " is made stronger by the contrast.

16. This stanza is not fast-moving. The repeated echoes of lines 5 and 9 tend to slow its pace. One could not imagine a tale of the type of " Lochinvar " told in it. But in this poem narrative and description are blended. It is hard to find a stanza that is devoted to pure narrative. The tale is told in a series of pictures for the careful painting of which the stanza offers room and time.

*　　*　　*

THE WIFE OF USHER'S WELL (116)

1. Ballads seldom indulge in description (see " Annan Water " page 38, and notes, page 153). We gather from the story that she loved her sons, and that she loved to rule. We are told she was old. Her fearsome wish tells both of her love and her forceful character.

2. The poet was interested in two things, the wife's wish, and its consequences. In the manner of ballad makers, he concentrates upon his theme. An account of the deaths of the sons would have distracted our attention, and possibly weakened the effect of the wish upon us.
Compare " Get up and Bar the Door " (page 36) and " Annan Water ".

3. She was old, she loved her sons, she loved power. The " word " that came drove her to a cold fury. The sea had taken her sons. Let storms endanger all sailors until her sons return.

4. Had her love power over the gates of Paradise and the grave ? Were they sent as a punishment for her rebellion against Fate ? The ballad is not interested so much in the reason as in the fact of their return. It neither teaches nor preaches.

5. From the other world. Their mother wished for their return in earthly flesh and blood. Though their hats were of the birk that grew before Paradise, the worm awaited their bodies. See also note 8, below.

191

6. She acted from love, perhaps also from fear, lest her sons should vanish. She would hold them against death and the grave.

7. One of the " maidens " is at her first duty of the day, as the sons pass out of the house.   They bid her farewell as they go.

8. Yes.   He lived at a time when belief in ghosts was common.   He has written in a simple manner, as though he were narrating an every-day occurrence.   He does not try to persuade us to accept his story, does not seem to feel that any such attempt is necessary.

9. See note 8.   The poet's simple sincerity grips us and compels our belief. It is a real house we enter. Most natural are the orders to set the fire ablaze, and to bring water from the well, most natural the mother's action in wrapping herself in her mantle as she takes guard by the bed-side, most natural the kindling of the fire in the grey morning.   The sons, too, are " real ".   They have still an interest in barn and byre, and in the bonny lass.   Even lines 41-44 come as a simple reminder of facts known to speaker and listener.   No one can forget this strange quiet way of describing the contact of the living with the dead.   It is a grim situation, but it is not horrible, for love of mother for sons created it. Human love and the mystery of the world beyond this are two themes of which readers do not tire.   They are bound together here.

Their hats were o' the birk (line 20).   Hats of birch bark or birch twigs were worn by men of older days, for the tree was thought to have power against evil spirits.   But this birch grew at the gates of Paradise.   So, when Kilmeny returns from " a land of love and a land of light ", she wears a " bonnie snood of the birk sae green ".   See Book III, page 27. Sir Walter Scott thought that the notion, that the souls of the blessed wear garlands, was of Jewish origin.   But similar beliefs regarding this tree are found in the legendary poems and tales of many lands.

*   *   *

EARL HALDAN'S DAUGHTER (118)

1. Like the ballads you have read, this poem has a spirited opening, takes us at once into the story and carries us along with speed.   It spends but little time on description.   " Long and loud laughed she " tells us all we need to know of the character of Earl Haldan's daughter.   The repetition, in lines 1, 2, 3, 9, 10, is a ballad device—compare " The Wife of Usher's Well " (page 116).   The refrain (lines 7, 15, 23, 31) is found in some ballads.

2. Here you must choose for yourself.   You may prefer that the rover drive home the lesson against pride, as he does in the poem, or you may prefer that he remain a rover, and that the moral remain unpointed.
Contrast " Magdalen " (Page 92).

192

PROUD MAISIE (119)

1. There is no " reason " for calling her proud. The question she asks has been asked by girls of all natures. But no other word would bring out so well the contrast between question and answer. We see her " proud " in youth, health, strength, confident in herself and her future, with never a thought of death.

2. Scott points no moral. Maisie's pride is not the cause of her death. And, though the poem says nothing directly, we are not the less aware of the stern truth that lies behind it, that youth vanishes " like a bubble on the fountain ".

3. The poem is complete. It would be as foolish to consider who Maisie was, or why she was in the wood, as it would be to ask a painter to show us her portrait. Scott does not portray her. In one word he suggests a picture, and leaves us to do with it as we choose. Compare " La Belle Dame sans Merci " (page 120) and notes.

4. We have lost all that can be lost—the ballad-like directness of the poem, the drama of question and answer, the sense of mystery and awe, the wood-music, the rhythm, the beauty.
The prose seems fantastic ; we believe in the poem.

*　　　*　　　*

LA BELLE DAME SANS MERCI (120)

1. " Wretched wight " has not the colour of " knight-at-arms ". The latter arrests our attention at once, with a suggestion of the romance of long ago. There is a hint of mystery in it also. It is more strange that a knight-at-arms should be " palely loitering ". See, too, note 4.

2. See also lines 43, 44. It is the dead time of the year between Autumn and Winter. The earth is bare and cold ; its fruits are gathered ; its beauty has decayed ; " and no birds sing ". See note 5.
The poet has not described the season in full. He has suggested it in a few brief lines almost in the manner of the ballads. Compare *When nights are lang and mirk,* " The Wife of Usher's Well " (page 116).

3. She was a faery's child, and the poet has mentioned only her faery qualities—long hair, light foot, wild eyes. He has left us to complete the picture as we choose. Compare note 2. See, too, " The Lady of Shalott ", note A. 4 (page 189).

4. " Pacing steed " suggests the power, the energy, the life, not of the horse only, but of the rider. Substitute some such phrase as " my horse's back ", and note how much you have lost. The poet has again dwelt upon the essentials. He has said nothing of the colour of the horse. Is yours a grey, a bay, a black ?

5. It is Summer, the time of garlands. The knight is in the meads, rich in flowers. Contrast lines 1-12 and 43, 44.

6. Picture it for yourself, if you choose. The poet's two words suggest its mystery. The fuller a description becomes, the less remains for us to imagine and the less mystery in the thing described. Compare note 3.

7. It was the dream that ended all happiness for the knight, destroyed all beauty. See " The Lady of Shalott ", lines 116, 117. Note how abruptly line 36 comes upon us, how the word " cold " takes us back to the bleak wretchedness of stanza 1. Compare the effect of " pale " in the following stanza.

8. (a) We are brought back to the bare misery of the first scene, to the dead time of the year, to the knight's despair. We understand to the full the hopelessness of his loitering. Do you see him, his face, his armour ?

(b) The sudden ending of the stanza suggests that all is over, that happiness has passed away, " and no birds sing ".

*   *   *

COUNT ARNALDUS (122) and LORD ARNALDOS (123)

1. (a) For the ballad's " At the rising of the sun ", Flecker substitutes " On the evening of St. John ". Both are good lines. The first makes us think of the strange ship in the silence of the morning, with the strong Mediterranean sun behind her. The second hints immediately at mystery. See the notes, pages 99 and 124.
(b) The difference in the length of the poems is explained by Flecker's omission of the ballad's lines 11-20 and 29-36. There the ballad tells us directly that the ship and the singer are not of the every-day world. Flecker, more in the manner of our own ballads, leaves the mystery to declare itself.

2. You must choose for yourself. The ballad suggests a grander picture. Flecker's " little ship " hints more strongly at mystery.

3. Again you must decide for yourself. Would you prefer to allow your readers to form their own pictures ? Do not the sailor's grey hairs make him appear too real for the strange story ? Note how simply in lines 11-18 Flecker makes us feel the wonder of the song.

4. Flecker's version of the story seems more wonderful because we are left to imagine the song. We are told only of its power to charm the sea and the wind, the fish and the birds of heaven. In " Count Arnaldos " we know the song and cease to wonder as to its nature. Note Lord Arnaldos does not ask to learn its secret, but " What song may that song be ? "
Compare " The Lady of Shalott ", note A, 4 (page 189).

5. See note 4. The ending of " Lord Arnaldos " seems to preserve better the atmosphere of mystery. Line 42 of the ballad emphasises the power of the sailor. Flecker's version is simpler and the song remains magical in itself, not as an " ocean secret " with a value to the man who knows it.

6. See the preceding notes. The ballad insists more strongly on our remembering the strangeness of the adventure. Flecker's barer version appeals because it makes no comment. We catch a glimpse, as it were, of the scene, and are left to wonder at its meaning.

Lockhart's metre is akin to that of our ballads, though he has retained the Spanish " tum-ti " rhythm. Flecker's is still more simple. Its regularity and the scarcity of rhymes help to give us the impression that we are listening to an old-time minstrel.

*   *   *

SEA FEVER (125)

In the notes below, " Line " (ordinary type) refers to " A Wet Sheet and a Flowing Sea ". " *Line* " (italic type) refers to " Sea Fever ".

1. (*a*) Neither speaker may " deny " the call. Both are genuine sailors with the sea in their blood, to whom " the world of waters " (line 15) is home. Both have braved the dangers of the sea, and are ready to brave them again. The hardships of the life have, indeed, an appeal for them. The wind has a song for each (line 19, *line* 3), though it blow a tempest (line 17) and cut like a knife (*line* 10).

(*b*) Though the sea has called to each, it is not with exactly the same voice. Cunningham's sailors are " merry men " (line 16) dwelling together in their " hollow oak " and proud of their traditions as Englishmen (lines 23, 24). The speaker in " Sea Fever " hopes to have a companion (*line* 11) but he looks forward to the loneliness of the sea (*line* 1), the grey mist, the grey dawn (*line* 4), the vagrant gypsy life (*line* 9). The beauty of the sea means more to him than to the sea-dogs of older days, or, at least, he is better able to express what he feels.

2. Probably you would not be happy with either. Only an experienced sailor could enjoy the life each poem suggests, and his choice would depend on his nature—his preference for jolly company or for the more solitary pleasures that come from sea and sky.

195

3. See note 1. Both rhythms accord well with the poets' themes and the spirit of the poems. Cunningham's speaker is a hearty fellow, glad to be at sea again with his shipmates. His pleasure and his confidence in his ship (lines 14, 15, 23, 24) express themselves in the cheerfulness and assurance of the rhythm. "Sea Fever" is a poem of longing, rather than of satisfaction. We hear in it the music of the lonely sea that the speaker loves, the long, almost melancholy, roll of the waves, the wind's song, the cry of the gulls.

If we write Cunningham's poem in long lines, we come close to the rhythm of "Sea Fever". Compare

But give to me the snoring breeze, and white waves heaving high

with

And all I ask is a tall ship and a star to steer her by

His shorter lines suggest something of the stir on board ship, as **Mr.** Masefield's seven-beat line suggests the sea itself.

Cunningham's "ti-tum" rhythm is regular, assured, more of a "company" rhythm—one in which many speakers may join. Mr. Masefield's lines have a seven-beat pattern, but into this pattern he introduces many delicate variations, like a musician playing to himself. Compare

And all I ask is a merry yarn from a laughing fellow-rover

with

And quiet sleep and a sweet dream when the long trick's over.

The stanzas of " A Wet Sheet and a Flowing Sea " end with a decisive note on strong one-syllable rhymes—actually, all on the same " ee " sound. Mr. Masefield's two-syllable rhymes—" shaking ", " breaking "; " flying ", " crying "; " rover ", " over "—have something of the music of the sea.

*   *   *

SEMMERWATER (126) and THE NECKAN (127)

1. Both deal with man's " hard-heartedness ". " The Neckan " treats the theme at length. " Semmerwater " turns swiftly to the retribution that followed the spurning of the beggar.

2. (a) " Semmerwater " tells its story in ballad language, simple, and, here and there, of an older day. It moves at ballad speed. It makes no comment, leaving its readers to pass judgment. The beggar's speech is introduced abruptly. Repetition is employed steadily (lines 1, 5, 6, 11, 15, 18-25, 27, 28, 31, 34). The impression it makes upon us is not

196

unlike that made by " Annan Water " or " The Wife of Usher's Well ".
The beggar curses the castle, with a terrifying anger, like that of the
mother when she learns that her sons are dead.

(b) The style of " The Neckan " is simple. Events are recorded in
quick succession (lines 17-60). The final stanza, ballad-like, repeats
the first.

See note 5.

3. (a) While the words of " Semmerwater " are simple in themselves,
they are used with more deliberate care than is customary in ballads.
The studied repetition of the " ee " sound in stanza 1 produces the same
effect of quiet as Wordsworth's

> *The green field sleeps in the sun.*   (page 83)

The picture in the last stanza has been drawn for its own sake. An
old ballad would most likely have been content to narrate the actual
ruin of the town.

See, too, note 4.

(b) " The Neckan " does not tell its story so directly as do the ballads.
We learn it as Neckan recalls the events in his song. A ballad would
probably cut out the words that introduce the speeches (lines 23, 25,
35, 55, 61) and would certainly omit the comments in " kind " (line 16)
and in lines 19-20, 61-64. The poem, indeed, " preaches " in a manner
foreign to the ballads. Contrast " Magdalen " (page 92).

4. (a) The four-beat, three-beat stanza supplies the pattern that the poet
has had before him in " Semmerwater ", but he does not follow it with
the regularity of the ballad. Not one stanza copies exactly the stanza
of " The Wife of Usher's Well ". By his variation the poet has given
variety of pace to his poem. Compare, for example, stanza 1 and
stanza 6. The first sleeps ; the sixth rushes downhill until its pace
is stopped, as though for ever, by line 26. Write the first stanza in regular
form and note how much is lost :

> *It's deep asleep, and deep asleep,*
> *And deep asleep it lies ;*
> *The Semmerwater lake so still,*
> *Beneath the quiet skies*

(b) " The Neckan " is written throughout in the regular ballad stanza.
While it is interesting to note the points in which a modern ballad
differs from an old one, it is well to remember that points of difference
are not necessarily points of weakness in " Semmerwater " and " The
Neckan ". We enjoy a poem, not because of its resemblance to another
poem, but because of its own beauties.

5. In " Semmerwater " there are five pictures for us all to see—the
" mickle town and tall ", the beggar from some other world than this,
the herdman's cottage, the crashing of the city down " the brant hillside ",
the " king's tower and queen's bower " where " fishes come and go ".
In true ballad-fashion the poet merely outlines his pictures and leaves
us to fill in the details. How do you see the city—with tall towers,
proud, forbidding walls, and sentinels in armour that flashes back the
sun ? Has your beggar an unearthly look, or is he simply an old, travel-
stained man for thoughtless people to scorn ? Who are the kindly
folk who give him food and drink ? Can you see and hear the city crash
to its fate ? Can you see it far below the quiet waters of the lake, a
lurking place for the creatures of the gloom ?

Arnold, too, suggests, rather than paints, his pictures, though he supplies
fuller details.
Think of Neckan, with his harp of gold, on the headland, the blue sky
above him and the green sea far below. Think of the splendour of the
wedding scene—the knights and ladies in their rich, bright clothes, the
surpliced priest, the Neckan and his bride. Think of his wife in the
green, shell-strewn halls of the sea. Think of the last scene in the grey
twilight, by the cool birch trees on the river-bank. Do you see the
scornful priest, his hard, haughty face, as he rides over the bridge on
his white mule, richly caparisoned ? Do you see the budding staff, the
change that comes over the priest's proud features as he realises what
it means ?

Your pictures must be your own. The note suggests merely some of the
forms and colours you may see in them. As you study the poems,
images blurred at first will take firm outline and your colours will become
clear.

*   *   *

<u>TEWKESBURY ROAD</u> (130)

1. It was a country road that led one only to little villages, a road that
still had dust upon it, an upland road rising into the region of gorse
and harebell, of shy-eyed deer, and moorland birds with their wild cries.

2. *Delicate* : delicately formed, graceful.
Mellow : shining with a soft light.
A-ripple : waving in the wind. Compare with this line Wordsworth's
dancing daffodils (page 94). What word would Wordsworth have
written in place of " seem " (line 11) ? See note 3, page 183.

3. The rhythm of the lines suggests a good swinging pace, as of a man glad
to be " in the keen cool rush of the air ".

198

4. In stanza 1 the poet thinks chiefly of the joy of walking, of going on **and** on, without questioning, in the wind and the sunshine.

In stanza 2 he dwells on the beauty and the peace of the road at evening, a road so quiet that the deer troop down to the stream beside it.

In stanza 3 he delights in the thought of coming to close contact with the earth, smelling it, feeling the rain on his face, sharing his joy with the waving grass of the fields.

*　　　*　　　*

THE LAKE ISLE OF INNISFREE (131)

1. It is a lonely, quiet island in a lake, heather-covered, with perhaps a little, willow-clothed valley. Here the cabin of clay and wattles will be straightway one with the earth in which it is set.

2. Listen particularly to lines 4 and 10. Like Shakespeare's magic island in " The Tempest ", " the isle is full of noises ", low sounds that fall softly on the ear and bring peace—the song of the cricket, the flutter of wings. Especially we hear the day-long hum of bees and the lapping of the lake. Listen to the " l " sounds and the vowels in the lines referred to above.

3. Why " kisses four " in " La Belle Dame sans Merci " ? To such questions there can be only one answer—that the poets chose to write so. If you care to read other numbers into line 3, you may feel that " nine bean rows " comes most smoothly and quietly off the tongue, and accords best with the peace of the island.

4. Lines 5, 6. These lines may suggest to you a picture of calm day-break. From " the veils of the morning ", the grey clouds that shroud the sun, to the heath where the cricket keeps up its steady, quiet song, peace falls slowly, gradually, upon us. If you think of the cricket by the hearth-side, in the evening, the lines will mean that peace descends on the island all day long.

Midnight is " all a glimmer ", for the lapping water reflects the stars. The light on the heather makes noon " a purple glow ".

At evening, the birds, undisturbed by men, fly to their resting-places. The rhythm of the poem brings peace to the ear. Listen to the three slow six-beat lines, and the concluding four-beat line in which the voice seems to die away as in a cradle-song.

5. See, particularly, stanza 3. The sound of the lake water has come to his ear with its promise of loneliness and peace, and called him from the crowds of the city.

199

6. In place of the dignity and the beauty of the poet's rhythm, we should have had one without claim on our attention or hold upon our memory.

The more we read, the more fully do we discover how strange a power words can have. They do not only " mean ", they hint at meanings, remind us of pictures and ideas which they have been used elsewhere to create. The opening words recall to us the cry of the Prodigal Son, in Luke xv, 18, " I will arise and go to my father ". They come to us with an added power and beauty because of their use in that moving and beautiful story. They suggest that the poet, too, has lived in " a far country ", and that now he is going home. Words are changed by the work they do, and the other words they meet, even as we are changed by our occupations and companions.

*　　　*　　　*

AN OLD WOMAN OF THE ROADS (132)

1. The life that would mean happiness to the **Old Woman** would probably be dull to most of us. In the poem we see the little house through her eyes—the eyes of a beggar, tired of bog and road, of mist and dark, of the crying wind and the rain. In her poverty she thinks of the house as something to own. Its clock and delph would be possessions to tend and love. In the cold and rain she thinks of its warmth and security, its peat-stack, its heaped-up fire glinting on the delph, its bed waiting for her. No longer an aimless wanderer on the naked roads, she would be at home and busy all the day.

2. Read it slowly, quietly, sincerely. The Old Woman is weary. The poem is her prayer.

3. To some extent your answer will depend upon your own circumstances, the life you have to live, the life you want to live. We pity most the Old Woman, because the misery of her life is made plain. She asks very little—the simple comforts of an Irish cottage as she has seen them so often from the doors at which she has begged—and her longings are expressed in her own simple speech. But, if we have read the poems, not with our eyes only, but with our imaginations, each poet has made us sympathise with his longing—whether for the hard life of a sailing ship, the freedom of the road, or the peace of Innisfree.

200

1. His interest is in the gallop. See the note, page 135. The news is of importance only as the reason for the ride.

2. Of Dirck we are told nothing. Joris seems to be a cheerful fellow, hopeful, confident in himself (lines 18, 42, 43) kindly towards horse and man (lines 31-33). Roland's master loves his horse as the poet loved York, and is careful of his welfare (lines 10, 11, 22-24, 49-53). But the gallop is the theme, not the riders.

3. The lines of the first stanza (call it A) contain each eleven syllables. The lines in question 3 (call them B) contain each ten. Check these numbers for yourself. But in A there are four beats and seven unaccented syllables, while in B the numbers are five and five. The beats in A are twice as far apart as are those in B. We imagine we hear the thud of the hooves on each beat, and A gives time for a long leap. In B the horses may trot, but they cannot gallop. Meanwhile, the important thing for you is that you *hear* the difference in pace. Read A and B aloud until you do.

4. (*a*) Say lines 34, 35 aloud. The regular beats in line 34 would fall thus:

Of her chest, saw the stretched neck, and staggering knees.

But " stretched " takes more time to say than most words, and, in addition, we are forced in reading the line to stress " saw " and " neck " also. Thus the pace is slowed down. Say the line aloud, and you will find that you must give time to those three words.

In line 35 we must give time to " sunk tail ".

In line 41 the last words all demand emphasis. We cannot say quickly " a dome-spire sprang white ".

In line 43 we pause naturally at the end of Joris's speech.

In line 44 the pause comes at " over ". " Lay " demands a beat.

You will observe that those slow lines describe the fall of the two gallant horses.

(*b*) Joris does not stop his horse. He is level with Dirck at line 31, turns in his saddle as he speaks line 32, and shouts line 33 back to him. " Stay spur " may be given as a sudden command. Line 32 is more gentle. If you shout the last sentence, remember you cannot shout quickly.

5. The first picture is of a misty sunrise, the second of a burning day.
The poet cannot give full descriptions, for his galloping horseman can
pay little heed to the landscape.   He chooses only what the horseman
would see.   In the first picture he brings out the " mistiness " by
picturing the cattle black against the sunrise, and the horse—the dearest
of all things to his master—at last becoming visible through the haze.
In the second picture he makes us " see " and feel the heat, as did
Roland's master.   The sun is " broad ".   It laughs pitilessly upon the
tiring horses and men.   The stubble is brittle with the heat.   The dome-
spire—white in the sun—" springs " into view.   Read line 40 and note
how it " crackles ".

6. *Leaped* : The sun does not leap up in Belgium as it does in the tropics.
But the rider is so intent upon his horse that the sun breaks upon him
through the mist before he is aware of its coming.   It blazes fiercely
almost immediately and promises a pitiless day.

Fierce : A horse's lips are not usually fierce.   But the furious pace is
beginning to tell.   The word makes us feel the strain upon the horse.

Lines 49-53 : The speaker does all he can for Roland, lightens his load,
pats him, cheers him on.   The stanza gives us an insight into the rare
sympathy that can exist between a man and his horse.

Stood : Roland has completed his work, and, like a long-distance runner,
who has breasted the tape, he can do no more.   No amount of description
could make his exhaustion more clear to us than this single, simple word.

1. We hear them in the first words of the poem, and as we run before them with the Cavalier, we hear them rather than see them in stanzas 1-4. In stanza 5 they are gaining fast on their quarry. We see their burning eyes (line 26) the sallow throat of the first knave (line 31), the gleam of swords and the flaming match (line 39). Rightly the author makes the Cavalier see very little of his foes. The onlooker sees most of such a game as this.

2. (*a*) The grey has more spirit than the roan. Compare his more fiery "Trap! trap!" with the heavy "Trample! trample!" "Thud! thud!" of the other. Kate is of rarer blood, and her feet move more lightly—"Pad! pad! pad!" Note the galloping effect of the mid-rhyme in the lines referring to her (3, 9, 15), the only lines where the poet has used it.

(*b*) Say aloud lines 13-14 and hear the noise made by the heavy horses in pursuit of chestnut Kate. Say them again, substituting "They broke" for "Splintered", and note how the poet has further slowed down the speed by opening line 14 on a stressed syllable.

Contrast

> *They splashed through miry rut and pool—*
> *Splintered through fence and rail :*

and

> *They splashed through miry rut and pool—*
> *They broke through fence and rail.*

A similar effect is produced in line 35.

3. In "How They Brought the Good News" the horsemen "keep the great pace". "The Cavalier's Escape" is a poem of flight and pursuit, of ambush, mêlée, escape.

In Browning's poem the riders "galloped abreast". The Cavalier is mounted on a lighter mare than are his enemies, a mare that breaks away easily and lightly, but at the end is hard put to it by the staying power of her pursuers, and saves her rider only by the spirit that can make a final effort.

In your reading you will bring out the changes of speed, but you will not forget that this is a race for life.

1. See lines 17-20. He is in school, compelled to think of far too many things (line 20) for a fine June morning.

2. The cloudless sky, the hill, the road, the colour on the face of the earth—all those come to his eye as he sits at his desk. The wood, too, he may see, but the burn and the splashes of sun on bracken and water come to his mind's eye, as the sound of the water to his mind's ear.

3. He is a fine fellow, so let us hope he will like many. In his present mood he may hear a friendly voice in " Sea Fever ", " Tewkesbury Road ", " The Lake Isle of Innisfree ", for his poem, too, is one of escape. He says he would like to think of nothing, but that is because he has at the moment to think of too many things. He uses his eyes and ears, and will surely approve of " Leisure " (page 14).

4. It is much easier to read the line than to talk about reading it. There will be a short pause at " lessons " and a much more definite pause at " whiles ". " Whiles " will convey much—that there is a time for everything, and that this is not the time for work. " —But in June ? " will be half question, half exclamation of disgust, or disbelief in all grown-up rules and regulations.

It may interest you to learn that when Mr. Bain wrote this poem he was, not a school-boy, but a school-master.

*   *   *

AULD LANG SYNE (139)

1. (*a*) It strikes a note that not Scotsmen, only, but all men understand, and that most men delight in. It is a poem of good-fellowship and the reunion of friends. It is sung at happy meetings to express the hope that many more meetings are yet to come. We have seen how people like to escape—to the sea, from the sea, to the open road, from the open road. Here they escape to a land that almost every grown man loves—the land of his boyhood and his boyhood's friends.

(*b*) Many beautiful poems make poor songs, because they reveal their beauties only to those who read them and think them over. " Auld Lang Syne " is an expression of deep but simple human feeling, a simple and direct expression, as a song should be. Its sentences are short and its rhythm is easily followed.

That is part of the secret. The other part, like the secret of the beauty of a bird's song, of a summer morning, of any poem, may be felt, rather than " explained ".

INDEX OF FIRST LINES